⟳ ACCELERANCE

Chuck,

I'm talking to companies in Boston about best practices and great "how-tos" for effective software outsourcing that solves the developer shortage. We could write a book about this … and we did! It's our business fable, *Outsource or Else!*

I thought you might enjoy a free copy. It's a fun and educational read (see reviews on back)! I also bookmarked a few passages to help you grok several key points.

Enjoy!

Kayla

Accelerance is a consulting firm that helps technology leaders create effective strategies for global software outsourcing through better planning, better partners and better ongoing management.

```
problemSolved();
```

Useful, practical advice for tech leaders

Outsource or Else! is the critically-acclaimed technology management fable written by Accelerance founders, Steve Mezak and Andy Hilliard. The book provides an entertaining, yet realistic look at the common concerns and pitfalls that companies face when navigating the risks and rewards of software development outsourcing.

What people are saying about *Outsource or Else!*

★★★★★ **This is THE book on Outsourcing.**

"If you're thinking of outsourcing or even if you already outsource read this book. As a CIO I recommend this book to anyone that looks to hire or to build a software development team."

★★★★★ **Key tips for outsourcing written in an easy-to-read and engaging style**

"A great read for anyone or any company considering outsourcing some or all of their software development (or even a great read for those not yet considering it). You'll find practical tips and straightforward guidance on making the transition from "in-house to outsourcing" a successful one. Easy to read and in an engaging format!"

★★★★★ **Not to cut costs but to improve your current team and build better software faster**

"Not to cut costs but to improve your current team and build better software faster. Having been an Project Manager in a company that outsourced development we did it almost the right way but a few more hints from this book would have pushed us to much greater heights delivering code faster and better."

accelerance.com

Outsource or Else!

How a VP of Software Saved His Company

STEVE MEZAK

ANDY HILLIARD

Accelerance, Inc.
Redwood City, California

Published by
Accelerance, Inc. Redwood City, California, USA

First Edition, June 2016

Text design by Bookwrights, wwww.bookwrights.com
Cover design by Kathi Dunn, www.dunn-design.com

Printed and bound in the United States of America

978-0-9778268-2-7   Soft cover
978-0-9778268-3-4   mobi
978-0-9778268-4-1   epub

Dedications

To my late wife, Paula (Fraraccio) Mezak,
who studied French and loved to travel.

~Steve Mezak

To Silvia, Sophia, Tomas, and Emily, who motivate me
to do my best and who put up with me.

~Andy Hilliard

ACKNOWLEDGMENTS

We want to thank the following individuals for the contributions and help they gave us while writing this book.

To Hugh Morgan, Michael McAuliffe, and Scott Pollov on the Accelerance team, thank you for the title suggestions, your encouragement, and your patience when we were distracted from work by our book-authorship duties.

Thank you to Ron Lichty, Andras Boross, and Rich Mironov for your initial advice about how to make the characters and story more realistic than what we shared with you in our original outline.

We are grateful to Author Bridge Media's Helen Chang for helping us identify the Seven Keys of Software Outsourcing, and to Kristine Serio for inventing Rick Looney, whom she claims is not a distant relative of hers. (He's not related to the authors, either!)

Thank you to Mayapriya Long for the excellent interior design.

Thank you also to Kathi Dunn and Hobie Hobart for an excellent cover.

Thank you Useagility for the design of the OneWorld iPad app on page 57.

We are grateful to Howard Greenfield, who helped to brainstorm the title and offered us ongoing encouragement throughout the book-writing process.

Our gratitude also goes out to everyone who voted in our title survey (you know who you are). Each of you can say that you voted for the title we actually used, because we'll never tell anyone how you actually voted (except maybe for the guy who suggested that we use *50 Shades of IT Outsourcing* . . .). And finally, to everyone who advised us not to put "Silicon Valley" in the title, we are in your debt!

CONTENTS

BurnRate

Jason Jaye swore under his breath and swerved left, dodging a red Honda as it cut him off in the turn lane. His fingers twitched, but he counted to five and kept them off the horn.

It was shaping up to be a perilous morning.

The road had been invaded by a flash mob of lunatics—he'd almost hit a reckless motorcyclist speeding between lanes in traffic on 101 as he guided his Prius out of the carpool lane to get to his exit a few minutes ago—but that wasn't the worst of it. The reason Jason was on the road this early in the first place was a two-line text message that had buzzed to life on his phone shortly after he'd rolled out of bed.

> Urgent meeting, 8:00 a.m.,
> conference room.
> Changes to BurnRate.

The message had come from ShapeShift's CEO, Scott Bolden, who was notorious for using texts like pagers rather than two-way communication systems. "What changes?" Jason had texted back. No response. So he'd skipped his morning bike ride, pecked Paula on the cheek, and headed straight into the office.

He posed the question to himself for the twelfth time as he made a U-turn at the light. No, not just "what changes." What *urgent* changes? In his year-and-a-half tenure as VP of engineering with ShapeShift, he'd never known Scott to be cryptic.

Please no new features. Not now, Jason prayed. They only had ten months left to launch the BurnRate product on schedule, and his developers were stretched thin as it was. Maybe Scott hadn't typed the message right. Maybe he'd meant, "Changes to BurnRate marketing plan." Or "Changes to BurnRate sales strategy."

Jason turned into the ShapeShift parking lot—just as a weird motorbike topped with a bright blue umbrella zipped across the entrance in front of him.

He gasped and yanked the steering wheel to the right. The Prius slammed into the curb and lurched over it, whiplashing Jason's head into the headrest. The green band on his wrist erupted in a series of piercing *beep, beep, beeps.*

The man on the motorbike continued on his merry way, unscathed.

"Christ," Jason cursed, and blew the horn. The biker, a wild-looking man with leonine white hair, paused at the street corner, flashed Jason a grin and a breezy salute, and rode on.

Jason scowled and dragged the back half of the Prius the rest of the way into the parking lot. The band on his wrist still shrieking, he swung into a parking space and fiddled with it until it shut up. The wristband—RunWay—had been his first product with the company. He'd never liked the beeper—especially because his tended to keep going off at random once it had been triggered.

It burst into shrieks two more times on his way to the front door.

"That makes three brushes with death before eight o'clock in the morning," Jason muttered, fuming at the umbrella-biked weirdo as he switched the beeper off again. "What's next?"

"Jason!" ShapeShift's CTO, Lance, fell into step beside Jason as he entered the office. Lance gave Jason a quick glance over. "Aren't you supposed to wait until *after* the mystery meeting of doom to look like hell?" he asked.

Through the pounding in his head, Jason perked up. "You know what it's about? The meeting?"

"Not a clue," Lance said. "Seriously, what happened to you?"

"A motorbike with an umbrella for a roof just ran me off the road," Jason confessed, rubbing the back of his neck.

The CTO guffawed. "Mary Poppins has it in for you, eh?"

"It was a guy."

"Barry Poppins, then," Lance corrected easily. He tapped the yellow RunWay on his wrist, identical to Jason's green one. "Hey, at least you burned a couple extra calories with your NASCAR driving. Maybe we should add 'dodging death' to our list of exercises."

Jason felt a smile tug at the corner of his mouth in spite of himself. "If that's the only change they want to make to BurnRate, I'll buy you a round at O'Malley's after work."

"You're on," Lance agreed.

They made their way past the familiar exposed ductwork, brick walls, and glass-faced offices lining the east side of the one-story building. In the middle of it all sat the conference room: a wide rectangle of floor-to-ceiling glass walls.

The others had beaten them there, Jason saw as they drew closer.

Michael, the company's round-faced, balding Chinese CFO, sat with his usual impassive expression in his seat at the long table. ShapeShift's VP of sales and marketing, Lisbeth, was settling into her place across from him, her blond hair swept into an uncharacteristically messy chignon on top of her head and traces of concern around her eyes.

Scott was seated at the head of the table, grimly reading something on his laptop. Scott had been an Olympic gymnast in his twenties. Jason could see every tense muscle in the CEO's huge shoulders through his jacket. Scott's lowered forehead looked about as heavy and determined as a freight train.

Not good, Jason thought, slipping through the glass door behind Lance and taking the chair next to Lisbeth. She nodded at him but said nothing.

They sat for several long seconds in silence, waiting for Scott to finish reading. Restless, Jason discreetly pulled a ballpoint pen from his shirt pocket. He started drumming it against his knee under the table.

Finally, Scott shut the laptop with a metallic snap and looked up at them.

"I met with the VCs last night," he opened bluntly. "We went over the numbers."

Not good, Jason thought again, drumming the pen a little faster.

"They're not good," Scott continued. "We've lost a huge amount of ground to the competition with RunWay. BurnRate needs to be a game changer."

"How much of a game changer?" Lisbeth asked quietly.

"A $50-million-in-revenue game changer," Scott said.

What? Jason stopped drumming the pen. Diagonally across the table, even Michael's stone-faced expression grew almost wide eyed for a moment. Scott went on.

"The online web application for users to view the data collected by the wristband isn't going to cut it anymore. One of the VCs got wind that the competition is already doing something similar. Users will be able to share info with other users, set goals, and communicate through social media. We're not sure if they're including a competition element like ours, but it's likely. We need to do better."

Jason didn't like where this was going. He closed his fist around the top of the pen and started clicking it quietly. *Please not new features, please not new features . . .*

"The VCs want new features," Scott said.

Jason winced. *Strike one.* He clicked the pen faster. *Please not* big new features, *please not big new features . . .*

"Exercise tracking alone isn't enough anymore. We need to take BurnRate further if we want to recapture market share. The VCs want to add the sleep-tracking feature from our product road map."

What? Jason's stomach dropped.

"The one we were going to release two years from now?" Lance protested.

"Yes. That one," Scott said. Then he set his jaw and dropped the real bomb. "They also want a nutrition feature. They want users to be able to scan their food and have the app calculate and input the nutrition facts into a personal total daily value tracker."

What? Jason stopped clicking the pen, his ears going fuzzy as Scott kept talking. Apparently, one of the VCs had a company in her portfolio that did image processing in the security services industry. They used it for face recognition. If they could identify faces, she reasoned, it should be a cinch to identify food, right?

Right?

Jason didn't notice that he'd dropped the pen until it landed on his foot. Scott—apparently done with his speech of death—looked across the table at him expectantly. So did Lisbeth and Michael. Lance, wisest among them, looked heavenward.

The shrieking beep of the RunWay on Jason's wrist went off again, doing its best impression of an emergency siren.

"*What?*" he blurted, swatting it back into silence.

Michael snorted. Scott continued to look at Jason over his folded hands, his eyes more piercing than the RunWay alarm.

Jason collected himself. Relatively. "They're crazy," he said as evenly as he could. "Do they have any idea what it takes to build applications like that? How many people we would need? And to finish it in time for a ten-month launch?"

"Six months," Scott said.

"No," Lisbeth protested.

"Yes," Scott confirmed.

"It can't be done," Jason told the table, his mouth settling into a grim line. He resisted the urge to dive for his fallen pen. Across from him, Lance went a shade paler—as if he and Jason had just become Spartans in arms, ordered to defend the suicidal pass in the Battle of Three Hundred at Thermopylae.

Except that there are two of us instead of three hundred, Jason thought. *Twelve if you count both teams of developers.* He did his best to meet Scott's freight-train gaze. "We just don't have the resources, Scott," he said reasonably. "They'll have to give us an alternative."

"They have," Scott replied. "They've offered to pull the plug on the next round of funding if we don't deliver."

Dead silence.

"You can't be serious," Lance scoffed. Scott leveled a
Lance fell back in his chair, mutely crossing his arms o

"Did they increase our budget?" Jason asked, reeling.

"No," Scott shook his head.

Jason's pulse began to pound in his ears. "Look, Scott," he tried, feeling more like a trapped animal by the second, "they've got to see reason. What they want isn't physically possible. We'd need at least twenty more developers to pull this off, probably closer to twenty-five, and you know we can't get them. I've been trying to hire even five new people for months. Our compensation isn't competitive enough as it is. Now they want me to fill *four times* that many positions at a fraction of the price?" He looked Scott in the eye. "We just don't have the people."

"We do need more people," Scott nodded. "The VCs think so, too. They want ShapeShift to outsource software development to make the new plan happen."

Another hush fell over the room. Jason felt sick to his stomach. *Outsource software development?* It couldn't be done. Not successfully. Everyone knew that.

Everyone, apparently, except their investors.

Once again, Lance was the first to speak. "Well, that makes it official," he scowled. "They have literally lost their minds."

Michael stirred from his statue pose. "We'll never stay in budget if we don't outsource," he said gruffly. He didn't sound happy about it. Not that Michael ever sounded happy about anything.

Lisbeth said nothing, her Portuguese features grim and silent.

The pounding in Jason's ears grew louder. "Listen, Scott," he pleaded, leaning into the table, "is there anything you can do? I'll make you a spreadsheet. You can take it to them and beg for more money. More time. Anything."

For the first time, a ray of sympathy appeared in Scott's eyes. The freight-train forehead eased up, and the gray at his temples seemed more pronounced than before. "I've already done the begging, Jaye," he admitted. "Trust me." He let one last hush of resignation settle over the group before he continued. "There's an Engineering Leadership networking event at the SAP office in Palo Alto tonight. They're hosting speakers on outsourcing. The VCs have asked that you attend. Can you make it?"

The seasickness in Jason's stomach rose to his head. He glanced around the table. No help was forthcoming. There was none to give. Forcing himself to take a breath, he looked back at Scott.

"I'll do what I can," he said.

The Next Rick Looney

Except that there was nothing Jason could do. Not really.

It was hardly a secret in Silicon Valley that software outsourcing was a game of Russian Roulette—one where the tables were turned, and every chamber of the gun held a bullet except one. Who wants to play?

"Let's not let them go quickly and painlessly," Jason imagined the conversation among the VCs that had led to this. *"Let's torture them for six months first and then destroy them."* Sadistic bastards.

He tucked his retrieved pen back into his shirt pocket and pulled out his phone as he left the conference room, heading to his office. En route, he brought up his calendar to see what else life had in store for him today.

Developer interviews, 9:00 a.m. to 12:00 p.m.

Of course, he groaned. Because the morning wouldn't be complete without a visit from Irony herself.

Jason pushed through his office door, walked around the desk, and collapsed into the low-backed ergonomic chair. He let his head loll back on his whiplashed neck and permitted himself the luxury of staring, zombie-like, at the exposed ductwork in the ceiling for a few long seconds. Then, with another groan, he roused himself and powered up his laptop to review the latest résumés.

Four hours later, Jason was in the same place he always ended up after interviews: back where he started. Or not far from it, in any case.

Two of the day's three job candidates had followed the usual pattern. Good qualifications. Sharp people. Had a lot to bring to the table. Decided they didn't want to sit at ShapeShift's particular table for Jason's subpar, non-negotiable offer of $100,000 a year. So they took their leave and didn't look back.

The third developer, Pete, was the first one in weeks who looked like he would actually take the job if Jason offered it.

Pete was a big Caucasian guy in his mid- to late twenties—"big" in every sense of the word. He had to be six foot four and 250 pounds by the way he barely made it through the doorframe of Jason's office. But he was soft spoken for someone who took up so much space. Pete had an earnest, easygoing attitude, not to mention terrific qualifications. He was very well versed in Java and knew several relational databases, including MySQL, PostgreSQL, and Oracle—even some NoSQL. His backend system development cred was unbeatable, and he was one of the few people who had answered Jason's puzzle question right on the first try.* In addition to Java, Pete also knew JavaScript and some Objective-C—not to mention another human language.

"You speak Spanish?" Jason had asked him, noting one of the bullet points listed beneath "other skills" on Pete's résumé.

"I was in the Peace Corps for two years," Pete explained.

"No kidding," Jason said, impressed. "My wife has wanted to join Doctors Without Borders for years."

---

* Jason's puzzle question to Pete: "You're given a function, 'foo,' that represents a biased coin. When foo is called, it returns a 0 with 25 percent probability and a 1 with 75 percent probability. In any programming language, write a new function that uses foo but returns 0 and 1 each with 50 percent probability." (See Appendix B for the answer!)

"Really? Hey, those guys are great. I crossed paths with them a lot when I was abroad," Pete said. "Is your wife a doctor or an RN?"

"Neither. She's a physician's assistant. Says it was the worst decision she ever made; they don't let PAs into the program unless they learn French or something." Jason smiled a little to himself, remembering Paula's indignation when she'd found out. "Where were you stationed in the Peace Corps?"

"Costa Rica," Pete told him.

"How was it?"

"Terrific. Amazing people. Really great food," Pete grinned.

Food looked like it was an important part of Pete's life. Jason had to admit that the guy wore the extra weight well. However, at a health-conscious start-up that made devices for staying in shape—where more than a few diehards roamed the halls at lunch hour making sure that everyone had organic spinach in their salads—Jason had to acknowledge that Pete might not be the perfect fit for ShapeShift's company culture.

In the end, he'd shaken Pete's hand and told him that they'd get back to him.

Now he was alone again . . . left to ponder the probable death sentence of software outsourcing staring him in the face.

Jason propped his elbows on the desk and put his head in his hands. Outsource software development. No one in his right mind would attempt it. Not this quickly. Not given the aggressive new plan. There were just too many risks—especially for someone who had no idea what he was doing as far as outsourcing was concerned.

And yet, taking on the new BurnRate features with his current team would be the equivalent of trying to move Everest with a forklift.

He sucked in a breath, sat up, and called his lead developer.

"Ravi, do you have a minute? I'm in my office. Grab Marion and meet me here, would you? I have some . . . news."

A minute later, a lanky Indian man in frameless glasses let himself into the office, followed by a pale, perpetually sunburned woman with riotous auburn hair—Marion, Jason's product owner.

Ravi stopped short in front of Jason's desk, took one look at him, and raised an eyebrow. "Have you been interviewing humans or ghouls?" he asked, and laughed. Next to him, Marion's already serious forehead took on a deeper crease of concern.

Jason shook his head. "The interviews aren't the problem."

He told them about the new improvements to BurnRate.

"They're crazy," Marion said, indignant.

"I know."

"We can't do it," she pressed. "We don't have the people."

"I know." Automatically, Jason pulled the pen from his shirt pocket and began tapping it lightly on the desk. "They want us to outsource software development."

Silence.

Then Ravi let out a low whistle and shook his head. "Well, that settles it: we're screwed," he said. "We may as well just start calling you Rick Looney."

Rick Looney. Jason knew the name. Everyone did. Ten or fifteen years ago, Looney's attempt at software outsourcing had crashed and burned his two-hundred-person company in a disaster so spectacular that he was remembered to this day—even though the man himself had slunk out of town with his tail between his legs soon after the fiasco's epic conclusion, never to be seen again. Rick Looney was the unquestioned emblem of why no one in the Valley wanted to go near software outsourcing with a ten-foot pole.

Jason gave Ravi a flat look. "Thanks," he said dryly.

"He's right, though," Marion pointed out quietly, twisting the engagement ring on her finger back and forth. "We *are* screwed."

Jason forced himself to set the tapping pen down on the desk— if only because it was the one thing on earth he actually had control over at the moment. "Listen," he told them as evenly as he could, "I need to come up with a plan of action. Scott told me to deliver a plan in seven days at the end of the meeting this morning. If you have any ideas, please, share them." Then, casting around for a way to end the meeting on a less dire note, his eyes landed on Marion still twisting her engagement ring. "How's the venue search going?" he asked.

Marion sighed. "Not good," she admitted, adding with a grumble, "Seven months isn't that last minute . . . you'd think *something* nice would still be available. All the good places I've called so far are already taken."

"You'll get something nice in the end," Jason said.

Marion managed a pinched smile. "As long as I don't have to get married at the Computer History Museum, I'll be happy."

"Really?" Jason said without thinking. "That place is kind of cool."

"Yeah," Ravi chimed in, "and the wedding party can all wear glasses with white tape on the bridge of the nose!"

Marion stared at them, deadpan.

Jason cleared his throat. "Anyway, I'll let you know if there's any news on the outsourcing thing. Thanks, guys."

Ravi and Marion had barely left the office when his phone rang.

"Jason, hi honey, listen," said Paula's voice when he picked up, "I need you to go home and meet the new landscapers. I can't make it back in time after all."

"Why?" he asked. "What's wrong?" In the background, he could hear blurred sounds of chaos in the clinic.

"Emergency," Paula explained. "Five young guys with a start-up—something about inventing more efficient rocket fuel. Anyway, they blew up their garage. All of them need to be put back together, my RN already left for the afternoon, and her replacement just called in sick. That leaves me to do the honors."

Jason's distracted fingers twitched for the pen. He flattened them on the desk and tried to focus on Paula. "Five of them? Can you handle that on your own?"

"Yes. They just need patch jobs—burn repair, a few stitches. One needs to wear an eye bandage for forty-eight hours. I'm thinking of stapling it to his head; he's clearly plotting to take it off sooner so that they can rerun their experiment." Paula gave an exasperated sigh. "They should make me an honorary doctor, for days like this," she added with a grumble.

"Hm? Right, stapled heads. Yes, I can meet the landscapers," Jason offered. His itching fingers gave up and seized the pen. *Tap tap tap.*

At the other end of the line, Paula's voice zeroed in on him like radar. "You're distracted," she said. "What's up?"

Jason knew better than to dodge her. He sighed and tapped the pen faster. "You could say that our VCs just blew up our garage," he admitted, and summarized the whole nightmare for her quickly. Paula listened without interrupting, the way she always did. "Thing is," he finished, dropping the pen altogether and raking a hand through his hair, "I honestly don't think outsourcing software development is possible. At least, not in this time frame. I don't think I can pull it off."

"Has anyone done it before?" Paula asked. She was in PA mode now: practical, unemotional.

"Sure," said Jason. "That doesn't mean they did it well."

"How many people have done it well?"

"I don't know. Ten percent, maybe? Five?"

"Then it can be done, and you can do it," Paula concluded reasonably. Her tone softened. "You're taking things too seriously again, Jay," she told him. "You always do. If this whole thing falls through, tell me honestly: what's the worst that can happen?"

The worst that can happen? Jason picked up the pen again. *Tap tap tap.* "Well, if we fail, the VCs will pull the plug on us. The company will go under. Everyone will lose their jobs. *I'll* lose my job. And we might . . ." He felt the blood drain from his face, and cleared his throat. "We might have to move back to New Jersey."

Dead silence filled the phone. Even the chaos of the clinic in the background fell quiet.

Then, *"What?"* Paula demanded, so sharply that he winced.

Jason didn't blame her. Both of them had loathed growing up in New Jersey. It had taken them years to get out. He glanced at the photo of Paula on his desk—one that he'd taken just a couple of days after they'd first arrived in California. She was standing on the pier at the harbor in Half Moon Bay, the late afternoon sun lighting her short, dark blond hair from behind. Her face was radiant, exultant. They had finally escaped.

Jason imagined what the opposite version of that Paula would look like, scowling from the boardwalk in Atlantic City, and shuddered.

But it was true: if ShapeShift collapsed, they might actually have to go back. He had a standing offer of employment there. Who knew how long it would take him to find another job in the Valley? Especially if he really did become Rick Looney: The Next Generation.

"Jason," Paula said, her voice low and grim, "listen to me. Software outsourcing will work. It *has* to work. You can do this." An unintelligible groan rose in the background. "I'm coming! You're not the only emergency in the world," Paula shouted away from the phone. "Wusses," she muttered under her breath.

Jason checked the clock. He'd have to leave now to be on time to meet the landscapers. "All right. By the way, I have to go to an outsourcing networking event tonight around seven thirty. They sprang it on me this morning," he explained as he tucked his pen into his pocket, grabbed his laptop, and headed out the door. "Will you be home before I leave?"

"Yes, I should be home by—*no!* Kid, I am warning you, so help me—do *not* touch that! Haven't you blown up enough buildings for one day?"

In spite of himself, Jason grinned. "You'd better get back to your bleeding rocket scientists," he said.

But Paula was already gone.

THREE

In Our Own Backyard

The landscapers were a motley crew.

Jason's drive home had, mercifully, been less eventful than the drive into work that morning had been. He'd pulled into the garage of his and Paula's Eichler house less than five minutes before the landscapers pulled up to the curb out front. They arrived in a dusty white van with "Mike's Landscaping" printed across the side in blue block letters. Four men climbed out.

Their leader, Mike himself, shook hands with Jason.

Mike's hand in Jason's was thick and coarse, and his manner was gruff and weather beaten to match—as if he'd spent so much time outdoors that dust and dirt were now part of his skin.

He looks like a coal mine boss, Jason thought as the introduction ended and their hands dropped. Of the three migrant workers standing behind Mike, only one would meet Jason's eyes. Mike introduced them next. The one with the steady gaze was Manuel.

"So, how long have you been in business?" Jason asked Mike, leading the crew around to the back of the house.

"Long time," Mike said, and offered nothing else.

A man of few words. Clearly.

Jason felt a flicker of doubt. But Mike's team had been vetted. He'd gotten the recommendation from Lance, whose friend had used Mike's Landscaping to install a fountain feature in her front yard. Mike was also fully $6,000 cheaper than the alternatives Jason had found online and could get started right away. Jason shook the feeling off.

Paula was always telling him to stop judging books by their covers.

They arrived on the back deck.

"Well, this is it," Jason said. The backyard was small and, at the moment, barren. Their wooden deck was the only finished piece of it. From it, three steps led down to about nine hundred square feet of flat space, which then turned into a sharp slope up to a neighbor's fence at the back of the property.

Mike nodded. Behind his shoulder, Manuel took in the lay of the land with a sharp eye. The other two workers looked bored.

Jason cleared his throat and unfolded two stapled sheets of paper that he'd tucked into his pocket before walking out to meet them. The top page was a rough sketch of the future backyard, drawn by Paula. Manuel edged sideways to get a look at it. "This is what we're looking for . . ." Jason began.

What they were looking for was nice but small—the "small" part of the equation being the only reason they could afford it. Right and center of the yard, they wanted to install a modest swimming pool, one with a little rock waterfall feature built into the embankment. Around the pool, the ground would be paved with wide, natural flagstones that would extend to the other side of the yard to create a patio area. Paula also really wanted a koi pond, so they'd worked that into the design, not far from the pool.

"We also want to put in two Canary palm trees over there," Jason said, pointing to the west side of the yard, "to block the view of the house up on the hill. And we'd like to add some nice lighting so we can be out here in the evenings." He flipped the stapled diagram to the second handwritten page. "This is the master list of materials we want to use. My wife priced them out and double checked them about a week ago, so the numbers should be accurate."

Mike grunted and pocketed the list.

"Do you have any questions for me?" Jason asked him.

Mike shook his head. "Nope."

"All right," Jason said. *I guess after you've landscaped a few hundred yards, you already know the answers to everything.* "Over the phone, you estimated three months to complete the job. Does that still sound doable?"

Mike nodded and, almost as an afterthought, grunted a low "Yep."

"Great," Jason nodded back. "When can you get started?"

"Right now," Mike said. He signaled the two bored-looking workers in the direction of the van, and they slowly shuffled off to get the tools. Manuel had a head start on them and was already halfway across the deck.

Jason felt his eyebrows rise. He'd already signed the agreement, true, but he'd imagined that they'd need to prep first. Take measurements. Draw up more precise plans than Paula's artistically challenged sketch.

Then again, what did he know about landscaping? Nothing. Less than nothing—most plants were too smart to even attempt to grow in New Jersey. He reminded himself again that Lance had recommended these guys. Anyway, he had work to do. All the work he'd dropped in order to be here to meet Mike's team, to be precise.

He wished Mike luck and headed inside to find his laptop.

Jason worked through the afternoon and into the evening without looking up from the screen. Around sunset, the noise coming from the backyard stopped, and he was vaguely aware of Mike's van revving up and driving away.

At twenty minutes past seven, he shut the laptop, grabbed a few leftover breadsticks from the kitchen, and headed out to the outsourcing networking event.

Paula, looking haggard from her rendezvous with the rocket scientists, walked in the front door just as Jason was rushing out. Jason's mouth was stuffed with a breadstick, and he was late. He squeezed Paula's hand by way of hello and hurried past her to the Prius.

"Is that dinner?" she called after him. "How were the landscapers?"

He waved at her in a way that he hoped said, *They'll probably have wine and cheese at the event* and *I'll tell you later.* Then he climbed into the Prius, backed out of the driveway, and sped off.

Software Outsourcing 2.0

lose to a hundred people were mingling at the Engineering Leadership Forum event when Jason first arrived. Almost all of them had stayed through the first two talks, about outsourcing manufacturing.

Now, the crowd was a shadow of its former self, as most people made their escape before the third and final talk: How to Outsource Software Development.

Jason watched the exodus from his folding chair in the right-hand side of the audience. The stragglers sticking around looked about as happy about staying as Jason felt. Even the wine and cheese caterers were packing up early, rolling a cart of bottles toward the exit.

Wait . . . Jason thought after them, feebly. *I need more wine. A lot* more wine . . .

He pulled the pen from his shirt pocket and began tapping it quietly on his knee.

The event host—a small woman with neat brown hair—took the stage. Discomfort was written on her face, whether from sympathy for the upcoming speaker or embarrassment that the Forum had invited a speaker on such an unpopular topic in the first place, Jason couldn't say. "It's my pleasure to introduce Patrick Delaney, president and CEO of One World Software Outsourcing Solutions," she said into the mic at the podium, and then quickly backed away.

There was a light smattering of applause. Jason stopped tapping the pen long enough to participate in it—then almost dropped the pen altogether when he saw the man walking onstage.

It was the owner of the weird umbrella motorbike—the one who'd cut Jason off that morning and almost landed them both in Paula's urgent care clinic—leonine white hair and all.

How's that for an omen? Jason thought grimly.

Patrick arrived at the podium and braced his hands on either edge of it, as if taking hold of the helm of a ship. He looked only a little less wild than he had on the motorbike, dressed in a loose, long-sleeved white cotton shirt with wooden cogs for buttons and a pair of battered brown loafers. The only reassuring thing about him was his eyes, which looked steady enough to cut through diamonds.

"Software outsourcing," he declared into the mic, speaking the words with relish. Delaney allowed the term to settle over the audience before he continued. "What is it?"

Crickets.

Patrick picked up the PowerPoint clicker on the podium and aimed it at the screen behind him on stage. It lit up with the One World logo, perched over a definition. "Software outsourcing is contracting someone else to do software development for your company," he read before turning back to the crowd. "That someone else might be down the street or international. In other words, software outsourcing can be domestic or global.

"But here's the real question," he continued. "Why would you outsource software development at all?"

Because your VCs have you up against the wall with a cutlass to your throat? Jason thought wryly.

"Wrong!" Patrick declared loudly into the mic, then threw his head back and laughed when everyone in the audience—including Jason—jumped an inch out of their chairs. "Just kidding, you might be right. I can't read minds yet. It's on my to-do list. Anyway," he clicked the PowerPoint to the next slide and gestured to the list of bullet points on the screen. "Ladies and gentlemen, without further ado, I give you: the benefits of outsourcing software development.

"Benefit one: lower cost, higher speed, and better quality," he began, reading from the list. He raised an eyebrow. "I bet you guessed the 'lower cost,' but 'higher speed' and 'better quality' are a surprise to some people. How is that possible?"

Again, no response from the peanut gallery.

"It's possible because when you outsource software development, you gain access to a large pool of talent and technical expertise," Patrick explained with a devil-may-care smile. Jason marveled at him. The man seemed either oblivious to or uncaring of the fact that his audience was reeking of enough skepticism to set off a fire alarm. "And ultimately, where does talent and expertise lead you?" he forged on. "To stronger products and better ROI.

"Benefit two," Patrick continued, "the ability to get good people fast. Some of you might know how frustrating it is to go through the long process of hiring employees yourself."

You think? Jason thought dryly.

"But when you outsource, you recruit an entire team quickly. That translates into delivering your product faster," Patrick said. "Benefit three: resource flexibility. You can quickly ramp up or reduce the head count of your additional resources, depending on the needs of your business.

"Benefit four: more innovation. Why?" This time he didn't bother waiting for a response. "Because your outsourced development team has the experience of working with multiple clients. They can share a huge amount of knowledge with you about what works and what doesn't, specifically for the type of software you want to create.

"And finally, benefit five: some really good Indian food!" Patrick concluded, and laughed uproariously at his own joke. One person in the back row chuckled with him. The rest of the audience was silent. Again, Patrick pressed on with his speech, utterly unfazed by the response. "Or, in fancier terms: expanded and enriched cultural experiences," he said.

Just what I've always wanted, Jason thought. *Maybe I can even get my very own umbrella motorbike. That'll keep the company from going under.*

Patrick clicked the remote, and the screen of the PowerPoint changed to a glowing green question mark. "Questions!" he invited. "Go on, hit me. What scares you about outsourcing software development?"

A long silence followed. Then, "Intellectual property," said someone on the other side of the audience from Jason.

It opened a floodgate.

"Loss of control."

"Cultural barriers."

"Unclear certifications."

"Communication challenges."

"Valid concerns," Patrick nodded when the snowball of doubt stopped rolling. "Better said: valid concerns about the *traditional* idea of outsourcing, or what I like to call Software Outsourcing 1.0. Which," he defined as the audience members shifted in their seats, "goes like this: 'I give you a task, describe to you what I want,

and expect you to do it as quickly and cheaply as possibl
Follow these specs and come back to me in six month
done.'"

Patrick grinned—a roguish, Cheshire cat smile that showed
all his teeth. "My friends," he said, "that version of outsourcing
was doomed before it began. This is the new world—'One World.'
Modern software outsourcing, or Software Outsourcing 2.0, looks
like this:

"*We* are going to deliver this software together—us and the
outsourced team. *We* are going to create a feature, review it, and
move on to the next feature together, all on the same page, one
sprint after another. Because the outsourcers are not the cheapest
slave labor we can find. They are our partners.

"You don't choose your partners based on who will give you the
cheapest price, alone," Patrick went on. "You're not looking for a
yes-man. Instead, you do some solid research and you find smart,
extroverted problem solvers who will take equal responsibility with
you for the delivery of your product. People who will take the ini-
tiative and challenge each other to solve development problems.

"And *since* you have chosen your partner with care, your intellectual property is safe, because these are people you know you
can trust," Patrick brought it back around, with a nod to the guy in
the audience who had brought up that objection. "*Since* you work
with them each step of the way, you never lose control." Another
nod. "*Since* you vetted them carefully, you know that they have the
security and development certifications to do what you need them
to do, and do it well. And *since* you got to know them before you
hired them, you know that you'll be able to communicate clearly
and work through any cultural issues that come up.

"It takes some real work to find companies that have an honest
passion for the art of software development. But they do exist. And
when you find them, your business will succeed." Patrick stood
back and seemed to look over the tops of their heads for a moment,

as if seeing his own glorious vision. Then he landed back on earth, sharp as ever. "More questions?" he invited.

A pause. Then, "I can understand domestic outsourcing," someone said slowly. "But how do you justify sending American jobs overseas?"

"Terrific question," Patrick said, flashing another Cheshire grin. "I'll let you answer it. Let's see a show of hands. Who here has lost their job or knows someone else who lost their job because of outsourcing?"

Not a single hand went up.

"Correct!" Patrick clapped once; the echo through the mic made Jason wince. "And do you know the reason for that? It's because the question of exporting jobs is a false issue. The truth is that the jobs are here—but the people aren't. We have a shortage of talent.

"Now, where do you go to find talent? Answer: you go where the talent lives."

He flipped through several slides in his PowerPoint and landed on a world map.

"What you find when you start outsourcing software development is that not all developers are created equal. The job you need to fill requires specific expertise, right? Well, different parts of the world excel in different kinds of software development."

Patrick forged on. "Now, here in Eastern Europe," he said, drawing circles around the region with a blue laser pointer that he had pulled from his pocket, "is where you find developers with great expertise in mathematical algorithms. Over here in Armenia, you've got your 'chess masters'—these guys are strategy focused. Bulgaria has the second-highest collective IQ in the world.

"Meanwhile, out here," the laser pointer skipped over to Asia, "India and Pakistan have a huge number of smart developers. Vietnam has some of the lowest rates around. And down in South America," the pointer hopped to the other side of the world, "Argentina is terrific for Agile development. Really, all of Latin America is nearshore. Great for collaboration during your normal workday. Mexico, Central America, and the northern countries of South America are all easy to travel to. And, most important of all," he grinned, "there's amazing surfing in Costa Rica.

"Any more questions?" Patrick asked.

The room was quiet.

Patrick nodded, as if giving himself a pat on the back for a job well done. "Just remember, kids: software outsourcing is not the enemy. It doesn't have to be scary.

"Outsourcing is really about hiring a company that's going to do a better job on your product than you could do yourself, hiring onsite people. That's the vision and promise of software outsourcing. Once you shift your mindset to see the whole global marketplace as your employee field, you're going to find some pretty mind-blowing employees. Thank you."

The scant audience gave him some even scantier applause and dispersed.

Jason pocketed his pen, fished out the keys to the Prius, and filed out along with them. He felt . . .

. . . a little better, actually.

The realization dawned on him with surprise. But it was true: for coming from an umbrella-bike-riding madman, a lot of Patrick's points made logical sense. For the first time all day, the stone of dread in the pit of his stomach grew just a little lighter.

Maybe outsourcing software development could actually be done.

Then, as he was passing the long-abandoned wine and cheese table, he overheard one of the engineers behind him mutter, "Yeah . . . tell that to Rick Looney."

And the dread sank in again.

Jason ran a tired hand over his face. Who was he kidding? New Jersey had his name written all over it.

Paula was going to kill him.

No—he wouldn't go back, Jason vowed, setting his jaw and closing his hand around his car keys in a fist. Software outsourcing couldn't be the only option. There was another way to do this. There had to be. And tomorrow, he'd figure out what it was.

He climbed into the Prius and drove home.

Paula was out cold when he got back, her head half-buried in her pillow and her mouth hanging open, snoring faintly. Exhausted, Jason crawled into bed beside her. She didn't even budge.

He could relate.

In the instant before he fell asleep himself, he thought, *In the morning, please let it all have been just a bad dream.*

". . . Jason?"

No . . .

"Jason?"

Jason cracked open his eyes. His neck was sore, and a low-grade headache danced at the base of his skull. Early morning sunlight pierced the bedroom window. Paula was already out of bed.

ShapeShift still needed to be saved from sudden annihilation.

He groaned, threw an arm over his eyes, and rolled over.

"Jaaay . . ."

Paula's voice. It was coming from downstairs. And it didn't sound normal—more high-pitched and strained than usual.

Jason sighed. Then, heavily, he pushed away the covers and climbed out of bed to go find her.

She was standing at the sliding glass door that looked out onto the backyard, staring. When he joined her, he saw why.

The yard looked like a tornado had slammed through it. Coils of pipes and tools were strewn everywhere. Off in the vague direction of the future koi pond sat what appeared to be the biggest gopher hole on earth.

"Is it supposed to look like that?" Paula asked. She was wearing her "calm PA" face, but the words came out slightly strangled.

For a moment, Jason just stood there. Then he said, "I'll call Mike."

FIVE

Blind Alleys

There was no escape.

Jason had been hunting for a way out of outsourcing for the past six hours. He had filled the wall-to-wall whiteboard in his office with pros, cons, alternatives, and rationales against and around it. He had probably almost broken Google with his relentless searches for alternative options. He had called everyone he could think of, wracking his own brain and theirs for some kind of miracle solution.

The closest he'd come to anything productive was a conversation he had had with Bill Venn, an old colleague of his who had gone on to join a successful EMR start-up.

"You set up your own software development operation in Bangalore?" Jason asked, half-impressed and half-terrified. "That . . . seems like a big step."

"It was," Bill admitted. "And honestly? With six months, you'd never make it. It took us a year to get our operation going. Granted, we needed three times as many developers as you're looking for, but still."

"It worked for you though, huh?" Jason sighed, tapping his pen on the desk.

"More or less," Bill said. "It took months to get a handle on the attrition problem, and the savings weren't as great as we had hoped. But at least we had complete control over development." He chuckled. "At least I didn't become the next Rick Looney."

Rick Looney. The name made Jason wince more with every passing hour. It didn't help that Ravi's bad joke from yesterday had become contagious. Everywhere Jason went in the ShapeShift building, all people said to him was, "Hey Rick," or "How's it going, Looney?"

He'd holed himself up in his office pretty quickly that morning.

Once, before lunch (which Jason had skipped), Lance had come in to discuss which NoSQL database they should use to store food images, for the new nutrition feature. The developers were split between Cassandra and MongoDB; the former had the highest throughput in terms of scalability, but Mongo had the easiest out-of-the-box experience for developers.

"I'll have to think about it," Jason managed, struggling to make room in his head for one more thing.

"You know what? Don't worry about it. I'll figure it out," Lance promised. "You've got enough to worry about."

Lance shared a little bit about the machine learning features he'd been looking into, and they also talked about whether they should use SOA or microservices in the architecture of the new product. SOA encouraged a lot more sharing of modules, but microservices enabled things to be developed more independently.

"Which is going to be a lot more important to us if we're working with an outsourced team from who knows where," Jason pointed out, adding flatly before Lance could reply, "Please don't call me Rick Looney."

"Our investors are the loony ones, if you ask me," Lance snorted, disgust on his face. "Have you found the emergency exit from this highway to hell yet?"

"Working on it," Jason sighed.

They had agreed that microservices was the way to go, then assessed which skill sets they needed on their side in order to deliver BurnRate's new features—an exercise that left both of them feeling even greener than before. Afterward, Lance had tried to help Jason brainstorm outsourcing alternatives for another half an hour, to no avail.

Lance had looked stormy when he first arrived in Jason's office. He looked even stormier as he left.

Jason knew how he felt.

Now, at three o'clock in the afternoon, there was nothing left to try. No one left to call.

He looked again at the list of features he'd worked out with Lisbeth and the marketing team.

- Device software that runs on the bands, tracks activities, sounds alerts, and communicates with the web app in the cloud when connected by WiFi or Bluetooth to a mobile app on a smartphone
- BurnRate smartphone app (iOS and Android)
- Web app (same features as mobile app)
- Image recognition (runs in the cloud)
- Nutrition database (licensed from third party for first release; runs in the cloud, returns info based on food name and quantity)
- Social sharing, ability for users to compare their activities with others, hold competitions, etc.
- Ability to see activity and eating history (with editing capability)
- Ability to capture food images using the smartphone app

The marketing team had wanted the band to be able to capture images, but the engineering team had drawn the line there.

They'd never make the release date if new bands had to be made with cameras inside.

They'd never make the release date, period.

Like moving Everest with a forklift, Jason thought for the umpteenth time, letting out a long, slow breath.

He sat tapping his pen on the desk, at a furious pace, for fully half a minute. Then, reluctantly, he brought up Google one more time in a fresh browser tab. Into the search bar, he typed "top 100 software outsourcing companies." He let the words just sit there for another few seconds.

Here goes nothing, he thought. Then he hit "search."

Within minutes, he knew he'd plunged down a rabbit hole.

The "top 100" companies would be of no use: they were huge, and it quickly became clear that none of them could offer Jason the small, technical team of twenty-five developers that he needed. Domestic outsourcing was out of his budget, and international outsourcing looked about as easy to navigate as the Talmud. None of the blogs and articles he read had any clear-cut advice on where to start, and most of them disagreed with each other. The Q&A responses on Quora were just a litany of "answers" from marketers touting their software outsourcing firms.

He remembered that one of the VCs had recommended an outsourcing company to Scott, and Scott had forwarded the email on to Jason. Jason dug it up, but could find nothing reputable about the company—which was located in the Philippines—online. One search for them even turned up a nasty horror story about shoddy code and missed deadlines.

After an hour of hair-raising, futile research, Jason gave up hope of finding an answer on the Internet. Strung out and at a loss, he did something he thought he'd never do.

He started reading through the spammy emails he was always getting from random offshore developers.

> Hi, Jason Jaye,
> Greetings from Vitality Infotech!!!
> VITALITY Infotech, an Offshore Software Development and Website Designing and Development Company based out of Indore, India. We have expertise in Web application development and Mobile application Like iPhone, iPad, Android and Blackberry. We recently developed app for "Papa Johns" Middle East region is a World #3 Pizza chain Company—

No.

> Hi Jason,
> This is Simon with Neptune TechnoLabs.
> The purpose of this email is to see the synergies between our organizations. Neptune TechnoLabs is focused on offshore outsourcing of Microsoft/Java/Open Source technologies, web and mobile applications—

No.

> Hello Jason,
> I hope you're doing well.
> Allow me to introduce myself. My name is Rahul, and I am with Intransitive Technologies. Since we are connected via LinkedIn, I thought to write to you to initiate a dialogue regarding our company services.Intransitive is into software product development, working with the team of experienced people in a domain expertise like Healthcare, Banking, Education and Hospitality, etc.
>
> Our service offerings include:
> • Product development in Java, Node.JS, iOS and Android

- Application testing and QA
- Continuous Integration and Deployment
- Cloud-based services like Amazon, Azure and Rackspace
- Big data, relational and NoSQL databases

We would like to share more details about our company services and expertise by scheduling a short call with you. Kindly respond to us and let us know your thoughts and convenient time to discuss about the same.

Thanks and Regards,
Rahul Kumar

Well . . . maybe?

At least they had a few key things going for them: the health-care experience, product development in Java, continuous integration and deployment, NoSQL databases. All of those things were on Jason's list.

Still . . . *Really?* said the voice in the back of his head. *This is the answer to our problems?*

His mouse was hovering over the "reply" button, on the point of contacting Rahul despite the voice of reason, when he heard a tap on the doorframe of his office.

Jason winced. No one who'd visited him today had come bearing good news. Glancing up from the computer, he saw Lisbeth standing in the door, holding a few sheets of paper in her hand. *It's probably an email from the VCs,* Jason thought desperately. *"Did we say you had six months? We're sorry, we meant four."*

But Lisbeth took one look at him and folded the papers in half. Her brother was a developer, Jason knew. She had a better appreciation for what went on, on the back end, than most VPs of sales and marketing did.

Lisbeth crossed her arms and cocked her head. "Twenty-minute bike ride?" she said.

Wordlessly, Jason shoved away his laptop and nodded. Anything for the chance to get out of his office and the outsourcing rabbit hole.

Five minutes later, they were riding together out to San Francisco Bay.

The day was warm, but scattered clouds kept the sun from beating down on Jason's shoulders as he pedaled after Lisbeth, first down sidewalks and bike lanes, then along the levies and grass-lined paths that crisscrossed their way around the bay. He'd missed his morning bike ride two days in a row. *Big mistake,* he thought, as the exercise and fresh air strained the stress from his mind.

Finally, he could think clearly again.

Halfway through the ride, before they headed back to Shape-Shift, Lisbeth turned off the trail to a small scenic point, separated from the water by a guardrail. They braked and took in the view, still seated on the bikes, with one foot each on the ground for balance. In front of them, the bay stretched away into the distance, vast and sparkling and untroubled.

Jason let out the breath he'd been holding for the last thirty-two hours and confessed.

"I can't do this myself. I don't have the time or the knowledge to figure out how successful software outsourcing works. If it works at all," he admitted.

Lisbeth was quiet for a moment, looking out at the bay. Then, "For what it's worth," she offered, "I've heard Patrick Delaney knows his stuff."

Jason's eyebrows went up. He shot her a sideways glance. "You know him?"

"Not me," Lisbeth shook her head once. "But he helped my brother's company outsource software development, late last year. It saved their project."

That, Jason decided, was the best news he'd heard all day.

"Good to know," he said. "I'll clear it with Michael and look him up when we get back. Hopefully he'll have time to fit me into his schedule tomorrow." Then he mustered a small smile and added, "Thanks."

Lisbeth returned the smile. "Hey, my job is on the line, too," she said. Then she turned her bike back onto the path, calling over her shoulder as she pedaled ahead of him, "Don't screw this one up, Looney!"

SIX

One World

This can't be the right place.

Jason was standing outside the old, long-abandoned train station. The building was shaped like a wedge, with a brick-framed ground floor and a wall of soot-stained windows—all of them divided by metal beams—on the upper one, where the old offices must have been. It was a neat place—but it looked like no one living had come near it in at least a decade.

He double checked the email from Patrick, then the GPS on his phone. The address was a match.

Must have been a typo, Jason thought. He was just about to head back to his Prius and contact Patrick for the right address when he saw it: a weird little motorbike with a bright blue umbrella folded at its side, parked discreetly to the side of the building.

Warily, Jason put his phone back in his pocket and approached the front doors.

They were made of thick, metal-framed glass like the windows on the upper story. Also like the upper-story windows, they were clouded with soot. Through the grayish-brown haze of it, Jason saw a temporary sheet of paper affixed to the other side of the glass with Scotch tape. It read:

One World Software Outsourcing Solutions

Terrific. He sighed and pushed through the door.

The space inside was decluttered, but barren. Patrick had clearly just moved in. No receptionist. Not even a receptionist desk, for that matter. The walls were empty, and the only seating consisted of a few rows of wooden waiting-room chairs, long bolted to the concrete floor.

There was no one in sight.

"Hello?" Jason called hesitantly.

The word echoed back to him: *hello . . . hello . . .* It lingered the longest somewhere off to the left—up a nearby stairwell, Jason realized.

He followed it.

The stairwell led to a deserted hallway on the second floor. Faded linoleum ran the length of it. He was right, Jason saw: these were abandoned offices.

Well, almost abandoned.

The door to the office adjacent to the stairs was open, and the room beyond was empty of people . . . but not of things. He turned and stepped toward it to get a closer look, standing in the doorframe.

It looked like someone had taken a world map, shaken it up in a jar—like a snow globe—and poured its contents out into what could only be Patrick Delaney's office.

Planted in the center of the room was a heavy, olive-brown wooden desk with an elaborate elephant motif carved into its front-facing panels. Around the desk, an exotic chaos of artifacts revolved like planets around the sun: two matching wooden chairs in front of it, and a more comfortable, high-backed brown leather office chair behind; a hanging string of woven baskets patterned with Peruvian designs, all of them stuffed with folders, staplers, and other incongruously normal office supplies; and a "lucky bamboo" in a heavy Chinese pot in the corner—one that looked more like a tree than a plant. Along one edge of the desk, four clay things shaped like giant eggs—each with finger-sized holes in their bellies and Chinese characters on their backs—stood guard, and underneath it all lay a zebra-skin rug that appeared to be the real deal.

There were even two framed pictures propped up against the wall, Jason noticed—the first he'd seen in the entire building. One of them was a photo of Patrick skydiving. The other was a shot of him zip-lining off of what appeared to be the Great Wall of China.

I can see why he chose the old train station for his headquarters, Jason thought—then he suddenly felt self-conscious. He shouldn't be here—not alone, anyway. Shaking his head once, he turned to go find Patrick—and almost collided with him.

"Jason!" Patrick greeted him, the lone word ringing through the empty hall as if he'd spoken it into a loudspeaker. He was dressed in the same white cotton shirt with wooden cogs that he'd worn to the networking event, though he'd swapped out the loafers for a pair of open-toed brown sandals. Patrick clapped Jason heartily on the back. "Good to meet you. Officially," he added with a wink.

"But, you—hello," Jason managed, struggling to regain his balance. "I'm sorry, I didn't see you."

"There's a restroom at the end of the hall," Patrick said easily, ushering him into the office. Up close, Jason saw, the older man's wild mane of hair was actually blond going on white. "Have a seat. I trust Ziggy gave you a warm welcome?" Patrick asked, with a nod at the zebra rug.

"Um—" Jason began, but before he could form a response Patrick let loose a belly-deep laugh that set the entire room humming.

"I'm kidding, chief," he grinned, falling into the high-backed leather chair behind the desk. "Mostly."

"He . . . Ziggy is filling in for your receptionist?" Jason guessed, lowering himself gingerly into one of the carved elephant chairs. His fingers itched for the pen in his shirt pocket, but he resisted the urge to start tapping it on his knee.

Patrick laughed again. "Receptionist?" he asked. "To keep the throngs of clients in line, you mean?" His sharp gray eyes sparkled. He looked, Jason thought, utterly unconcerned about the lack of clientele.

But he had to have clients from somewhere. Right?

"So . . ." Jason cleared his throat. "How long have you been in the software outsourcing business, Patrick?"

"More than ten years," Patrick told him. "I've been a nomad for most of them. Why stay in one place when your clients are everywhere, and you can conduct your meetings from anyplace in the world by video call, am I right?" He smiled. "But, as it turns out, even I wanted a place to settle down eventually. Couldn't think of a more perfect spot for it than the Valley."

Perfect spot, huh? Jason thought. He was torn. On the one hand, it probably boded well that the guy had been able to keep his business going strong for ten years. Then again, Patrick's choice to set up shop in Silicon Valley didn't make much business sense, judging by his reception at the networking event a couple of nights ago. Not to mention the empty office. "What brought you to the Valley?" Jason asked.

"If you're trying to glare me out of town, it won't work," Patrick said, obviously amused.

Jason realized that he'd narrowed his eyes—a side effect of figuring out complex problems. He made a conscious effort to relax them. "Sorry," he said. "I'm just curious. Software outsourcing is a tough sell around here."

"Did you come to view my rare Chinese flute collection?" Patrick countered with a sweeping gesture at the strange clay knickknacks on the edge of his desk. If anything, he looked more amused than before.

Jason felt a prickle of irritation. "Look," he said, "no offense, but I'm only here because I have no other choice. Most people I know in the Valley won't touch software outsourcing with a ten-foot pole. Not after what happened to Rick Looney."

The name rang a bell. Patrick leaned back in his chair and hooked his hands behind his head, letting his elbows jut out. "The infamous Rick Looney," he said softly. He gave Jason an appraising look. "Tell me, Mr. Jaye: Do you know *why* Looney crashed and burned the way he did, all those years ago?"

Jason fought down the urge to reach for his pen again, under Patrick's even stare. "I've never heard the specifics," he admitted.

He breathed an inaudible sigh of relief when Patrick's face lightened up again. "Well then, allow me to enlighten you, Grass-hopper," Patrick said, and launched into the story.

"Rick Looney was the founding VP of engineering at a start-up. The company was originally well funded. Their task was to create an online web application: a business-to-business app called a Commerce Interchange. This was in the dot-com era. The app was designed to replace EDI and fax machines. It would route purchase orders, change orders, and shipment notices between buyer and seller companies using . . . *the Internet*." He pulled one hand from behind his head long enough to draw a smooth, sweeping horizontal line through the air in front of him, as if he were transferring the information with his fingers. Then he smiled and continued. "Rick was a lot like you, young Jason . . ."

So I've been told, Jason thought dryly.

". . . he was a good programmer, and he had a lot of domain experience. But he had no experience with offshore software developers. So he did what most people who have no experience do: he asked around to see if anyone knew a good company to work with,"

Patrick said. "And, as luck would have it, an Indian developer he'd worked with at his last company recommended a firm in India.

"Rick trusted the Indian developer who gave him the reference, so he didn't bother evaluating the company himself. He just hired them and got to work."

Patrick let out a long sigh. "Big mistake.

"After a couple months, he realized that the company was a bad choice. Progress was minimal. Communication was terrible. One developer in India left the outsourced team altogether and didn't tell anyone—not even the company itself. Rick was stranded and confused for a week before he found out.

"He knew he had to switch providers."

Patrick stretched, and continued. "So Rick asked around again and got another recommendation, this one from an investor in his company. The team was based in China. This time, Rick knew better than to move forward on blind trust alone. He talked to the leadership of the potential outsourcing team remotely, by video conference, and got the lowdown on exactly who his developers were going to be. The leadership introduced him to the developers. And, behold!" Jason jumped as Patrick raised his voice and threw his arms out wide, as if welcoming a chorus of angels into the story. Patrick laughed at him and continued, "They were all senior, productive developers. No question about it: Rick had the A-Team behind him now."

Patrick returned his hands to their station, linked behind his head. "Unfortunately for Rick, it didn't last.

"Over the next two months, his A-Team developers were slowly swapped out, replaced with B-Team developers. The new develop-ers weren't exactly high-level problem solvers. They needed daily guidance and direction. Guess who had the honor of supplying that direction, Jason?"

Jason raised an eyebrow. "Looney?"

Patrick grinned, and Jason thought he heard the rumble of a chuckle in the older man's throat. "Correct, Grasshopper. Rick himself gave them guidance. Usually that meant working late into the night, Silicon-Valley time.

"Before long, he'd turned into a zombie. Progress was once again inching along, and he was over-stressed, over-budget, and running into some serious delays. Rick decided that this arrangement wasn't going to cut it, either."

Patrick reclined further in his chair and propped his sandaled feet up on the desk corner. "And so, our good friend Rick switched providers for a third and final time. This new company, Rick knew, was absolutely, 100 percent safe: it was an American-run company with operations in India, South America, and Eastern Europe. Their rate was higher, but by then he was willing to pay it. Anything to get the project done.

"So he started over again with the American-run company. True, progress was slow—but progress *was* made. Eventually—finally—the product was done. Rick showed it to his management team."

Patrick unhooked his hands from behind his head and folded them over his stomach. "And the management team hated it."

Jason noticed that he was leaning forward in his chair a little, in spite of himself. "They *hated* it?" he asked.

Patrick snorted. "In a word, yes. The software was buggy and missing features that were supposed to be included—not to mention that they were long past the release date that the outsourcing company had agreed to. Bottom line, they refused to pay the company's expensive invoices."

"At all?" Jason said.

"At all," Patrick confirmed. "Which," he went on, "was when the outsourcing company decided to hold the source code hostage. 'You don't pay us, you don't get your code.'"

Jason gaped.

"But it was too late to start over again from scratch," Patrick continued. "Rick's only hope was to get his hands on the subpar code from the American-run company and take it somewhere else to continue development—something he couldn't do while it was being held hostage. In the end, his company was forced to fork over $50,000 in development fees for bad work."

Jason sat back in his chair and crossed his arms. "Wow."

"Yeah. Wow," Patrick agreed. "That turned out to be the killing blow. With all of the delays and cost overruns, Rick's company couldn't close funding—even before the downturn in March of 2000. Everyone lost their jobs, and, as you can imagine, Rick wasn't the most popular guy in town after that. People weren't exactly inviting him to cocktail parties and offering him new positions at other companies." Patrick sighed. "He left the Valley with his tail between his legs . . ."

". . . never to be heard from again," Jason muttered.

Patrick laughed and nodded. "Never to be heard from again," he repeated. "You have kids?"

"No," Jason shook his head.

"Shame. You sure know how to wrap up a fairytale." Patrick grinned at him.

"I'm not sure the story's over," Jason admitted. He *had* been crowned the Rick Looney of ShapeShift, after all.

Patrick dropped his feet from the desk and leveled the most straightforward look at Jason that Jason had seen on him yet. "It is over," he said. "None of the things that happened to Rick have to happen to you."

Then he leaned back in his chair again, all the devil-may-care lightness restored to his face, and added, "Old Rick did the rest of us an invaluable favor. He showed us what *not* to do."

"I can see why he's still famous, after all this time," Jason said.

"So can I," Patrick agreed. "You might say I came to the Valley to clear his name."

Jason's eyebrows went up. "Really? Why?"

Patrick's eyes softened, just slightly, at the corners. "I knew him, poor devil. We used to be good friends." Then he shook it off. "I consider it a personal challenge to reform the Valley's bias against software outsourcing," he declared, and cocked his head at Jason. "Starting with you. Hit me: Where are you at in your search for a good outsourcing team?"

Jason felt his face grow warm. But there was no way around it. He pulled Rahul's email—which he'd printed and brought along to the meeting—out of his pocket. "Well," he said, passing it over the desk to Patrick, "these guys offer some of the things I need."

Patrick took the email and scanned the first few lines. Then he laughed so uproariously that the windows actually shook in their panes, crumpled the page into a ball, and tossed it across the room into an African pot that looked far too nice to be a wastebasket.

"We'll begin at the beginning, then," he proclaimed, reaching behind him into one of the hanging Peruvian baskets. For all that they looked like a disorganized mess to Jason, Patrick found the folder he wanted without any fishing around. He pulled a single sheet of paper from it and pushed it across the elephant desk toward Jason.

Jason picked it up and read:

The Seven Keys of Software Outsourcing

1. Great developers are everywhere
2. Focus on your vision
3. In-person investigation is critical
4. Quality matters as much as price
5. Think like a partner and embrace cultural differences

6. The relationship is as important as technical requirements and capabilities
7. Everything you invest in hiring a good outsourcing team will return to you threefold

"Right," Jason said flatly, looking up. "I have a problem with number one."

Patrick grinned his devil-may-care grin. "You would."

"I'm sorry?"

"I've worked with a few VPs of engineering in my day, chief. Why don't you stop bouncing that pen on your knee and relax for a second?"

Jason flushed. He hadn't even noticed that he'd pulled it out. Quickly, he stowed the pen back in his shirt pocket. "I spent all day yesterday searching for great developers. If they're really everywhere, then they're in hiding."

"Not in hiding," Patrick countered. "You just have to know where to look. Once you do, you'll be surprised at the incredible talent you find."

"Really." Jason couldn't keep the skepticism out of his voice.

"Really," Patrick said, unfazed.

"Look," Jason told him, "I know I'm not going to get the same quality developers that I'd be able to hire here. Just level with me: At best, what can I expect of these people?"

Patrick lifted an eyebrow. "What you can expect from the *right* people is a whole lot of experience, education, and innovation," he said. "The people you're looking for aren't just maintenance programmer grunts. They're highly trained, and they have very advanced knowledge. They actually *want* a challenge. They've attended top universities all over the world. In fact," he added, "a lot of them have been trained in top US universities."

Jason crossed his arms. "Fine. Let's say these people really exist. Anyone can claim they have great qualifications. Why should you trust what they tell you?"

"You don't," Patrick said. "You do good research so that you know they're telling the truth about being capable. We have resources for that." He leaned back in his chair again and steepled his fingers. "Truth is, chief, trust isn't really your problem. Your problem is that you don't want to give up control of the development itself."

"This might come as a shock to you," Jason said dryly, "but controlling development is kind of my job."

"Wrong." Patrick reached for one of the egg-shaped Chinese flutes on the desk, tossed it into the air, and caught it again with one hand. "Your job is to *focus on your vision,*" he said pointedly.

Jason glanced down at the second key of outsourcing on the list, then back up at Patrick. "I envision a world where everything in development is under control," he said.

"But not under *your* control," Patrick specified. "Software development is a complex process. If you want good results fast, you need a team of talented people. Not one rock star developer, and definitely not one overworked VP of engineering. If you spend 90 percent of your time just figuring out how to build your product, and only 10 percent on delivering it, you're going to get stuck in the weeds."

Patrick must have seen the tension in Jason's face, because he sighed, set the Chinese flute back on the desk, and looked him in the eye. "Look, Jason, tell me honestly: How has it been working out for you so far, trying to do everything yourself?"

Jason looked at him. He thought about the months of struggling to hire more people without success. He remembered all the late days and nights he'd already put into helping BurnRate meet its sprint goals to cover the gap, even when they were still on the ten-month deadline.

He shifted in his elephant chair. There was no denying that he was sitting on a zebra rug talking to a man in weird clothes, who drove an even weirder motorbike with a blue umbrella.

But, at least at this moment, there was also no denying that the guy made sense. At least at the moment, the look on Patrick's face was a lot more lucid than crazy.

You didn't come here to prove a point, Jason reminded himself. *You came because you need the help. And this guy has helped a lot of people with the same doubts you have.*

He relented.

"Okay, you win," Jason said. "Where do I start?"

Patrick gave a roguish smile. "I thought you'd never ask."

He asked Jason a few questions about ShapeShift's specific needs from an outsourcing partner. Jason named the must-haves on his list: product development in Java, continuous integration, NoSQL databases, experience with image recognition and machine learning—"Our CTO has some experience with those, but he can't do all the development," Jason noted—and preferably medical device experience.

"Not just 'preferably' on the device experience," Patrick corrected him. "You want a team who has recently done the kind of work you need—or close to it. Otherwise you're breaking new ground, and that's a risk you don't need to take."

Jason took notes on everything else he needed to do during his preliminary research. He had to get references from the company's other clients, present, past, and recent. He had to get a cost proposal by email. "That'll be negotiable," Patrick said, "especially if you commit to a longer time frame of working together. Make sure it breaks down exactly which developer roles will be hired over a specific period of time."

"All right." Jason made the note. "What else?"

"Don't pre-judge your potential countries," Patrick warned. "Remember key number one: great developers are everywhere."

"Okay." Jason glanced over his list and frowned. "How do I actually *find* teams that meet all of my technical requirements? Please tell me this doesn't involve Google."

"It's your lucky day, chief. I've got a database for you." Patrick reached behind the desk and pulled out a laptop. He opened it, booted it up, and brought up the database. Then he turned the screen sideways so that Jason could see. "Everyone on this list has been pre-vetted by One World. They're the real deal. I'll show you how to use it. Then you're going to take the login info with you and do a little homework assignment for me over the weekend."

Twenty minutes later, Jason had an understanding of the database, a mission to create a shortlist of companies from it that met ShapeShift's criteria, and an appointment to meet Patrick for lunch on Monday to go over the results.

"Don't get overwhelmed," Patrick cautioned as Jason shook his hand and rose to leave. "You spend enough time in that database without coming up for air, you're gonna start to feel like Tom Hanks in *Castaway*, wondering which one of those hundreds of companies is your Wilson."

Jason conceded a chuckle. "I'll keep that in mind. Thanks for all this."

"Anytime."

Jason left the office and headed back down the stairwell. A healthy heap of skepticism was still floating around in his mind. But he had to admit it: the desperation and confusion had shown themselves out.

A few seconds before he made it out the front door of the railway station, the round, hollow tones of a clay Chinese flute floated down from upstairs, eloquently. Jason shook his head and, with a small smile that caught him off guard, pushed past the taped-up One World sign into the parking lot.

SEVEN

A Precarious Landscape

One thing was clear: Jason and Paula were in for a long three months with these landscapers.

Mike's team was disorganized, to say the least. They had started to dig the koi pond in the wrong place. Then they'd dug it in the right place, but installed the water circulation system wrong. Ironically, this turned out to be a good thing, because when they pulled everything back out of the ground, Paula discovered that they'd put in the wrong water filter.

"It doesn't filter out chlorine," she fretted, incensed. "Even traces of it will poison the koi. They almost killed the fish I don't even own yet, Jason."

"Good thing you caught it," Jason said. What he didn't add was: *If they can screw up a pond this badly, what can they do with a full-blown swimming pool?* He decided he didn't want to find out.

The silver lining was Manuel.

Manuel alone seemed to know what he was doing. He didn't talk much, but he worked hard. Jason often saw him in the backyard after the others had gone home for the day, attempting to tidy up some of the wreckage his fellow workmen had left in their wakes.

Manuel was good at cleaning up after the other landscapers' problems in general, actually.

Whenever something went wrong, Jason learned to go in search of him. He'd explain the issue, and Manuel would listen closely, without interrupting. "Sorry," he'd say, quietly, when Jason had finished. "Sorry." Then, just as quietly, he'd go and fix the problem.

Unfortunately, Manuel was outnumbered.

In addition to the two bored-looking workers Jason had met along with Mike and Manuel that first day, three new ones with similar apathetic facial expressions had shown up to work on the backyard that week. One of them, a young man named José, had stopped showing up on Thursday. No one seemed to know where he'd gone.

"I'll replace him," Mike said when Jason brought up the disappearance.

"Does this kind of thing happen often?" Jason asked, too tired to keep his voice light.

Mike grunted. "Migrant workers," he grumbled. "What are you gonna do?"

EIGHT

Does Canada Count?

Jason spent the weekend buried in the One World database.

Patrick was right: it was easy to get overwhelmed if you didn't come up for air now and then. Jason was actually grateful for the occasional distractions: bursts of noise from the landscapers in the backyard on Saturday and Paula plugging away at French verbs on Rosetta Stone on Sunday, as bent as ever on her quest to elbow her way into Doctors Without Borders.

"At least it's French," she'd told Jason once, "and not something insanely complex, like ancient Sanskrit." Jason sometimes suspected she loved France as much as she loved him. She had a habit of ordering expensive French takeout for dinner. "Well," she said pointedly whenever he objected, "maybe if you took me to Paris like you *said* you would, I could get it out of my system."

The Paris trip was a honeymoon idea that had been on the backburner for years, always postponed in favor of the financial burden of the moment: wedding loans, student loans, moving to California, buying the house, and, now, landscaping the backyard. All valid delays, but it was no secret that Jason wasn't especially enthusiastic about going to France. Or about going anywhere, really.

Bottom line: most of the time, he refrained from objecting to the French takeout.

When Monday arrived, Jason gathered the fruits of his labor and went to meet Patrick for lunch in Mountain View.

He parked his Prius on the curb outside a Turkish and Mediterranean place on Castro called Ephesus. Patrick had chosen the restaurant. Apart from Paula's French takeout, Jason stuck to American food whenever possible. Left to his own devices, this meeting probably would've been scheduled at Hobee's.

He tucked his laptop under his arm, locked the car, and walked into the restaurant.

Ephesus was small and had a contemporary look to it: glass walls, wooden tables, red mood lighting, and coral accents. Only a handful of people were scattered around the room. Even if the place had been packed to the gills, however, Patrick would've been easy to spot.

He was sitting ramrod straight, alone at a table with his eyes closed, wearing his customary white cotton shirt with wooden cogs. His left elbow was propped in the palm of his right hand, and his left hand was in front of his face, the thumb and ring fingers rapidly taking turns holding down either of his nostrils while he exhaled a series of short, loud breaths. With each breath, his cheeks puffed out. The noise sounded like air being pumped into a soccer ball. Then, as the other restaurant-goers openly stared, he stuck his thumbs in his ears, elbows jutting straight out on either side of his head, and began to inhale through his nose . . . humming.

Jason stood where he was for a moment, torn. There was a chance that Patrick was experiencing a medical emergency. However, there was an even better chance that Patrick was just being Patrick.

Gingerly, he approached the table and cleared his throat. "Are you all right?" he asked, caution in the words.

Patrick opened his eyes and grinned. "Jason!" he said, loud enough to introduce Jason to the whole restaurant. "Have a seat. You've never seen pranayamas before?"

Jason hesitated. Everyone in the restaurant was looking at them. But the moment for escape had passed. He lowered himself into the chair across from Patrick, who, as usual, seemed impervious to the weird looks he was attracting.

"No, I haven't heard of them," Jason admitted. He was almost afraid to ask. "What are pariah yams?"

Patrick laughed his window-rattling laugh, and Jason winced as the other restaurant-goers fired another round of weird looks in their direction. "Pranayamas," Patrick repeated. "Ancient Indian yogic breathing exercises. They're good for you: oxygenate the blood, calm the mind, help you achieve transcendence—all that jazz. I'll teach you sometime."

"I'm good," Jason said quickly, and changed the subject. "I did the homework assignment."

"Good," Patrick nodded. "And?"

"I've found eleven companies that look like they have potential," Jason told him. He opened the laptop and brought up his list. "But . . ."

"But?" Patrick prompted.

"I'm not sure what to do from here. They all meet my necessary requirements." He looked at Patrick. "I'm guessing you're not going to blindfold me, spin me in circles, and tell me to pin the tail on the donkey." *Although*, he added to himself, *would I really be surprised?*

"Good guess," Patrick commended him. He reached into the brown leather bag beside his chair and pulled out an iPad. "Behold: the One World Partner Selection App," he said, sliding the tablet across the table to Jason.

Jason picked it up and looked it over.

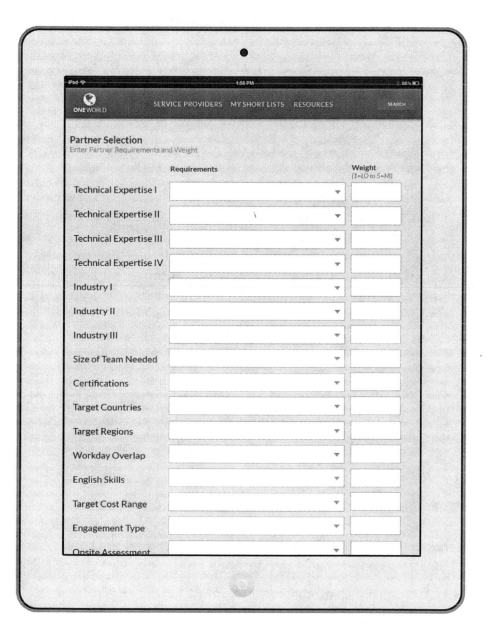

"Wow," Jason said when he reached the bottom, impressed.

"Yes," concurred Patrick. "Some of my finest work, if I do say so myself."

The corner of Jason's mouth twitched with a smile. "You'll have to explain the 'weight' column to me," he said.

"Swipe to the next page," Patrick told him.

Jason did. It had a list of all the pre-vetted service providers in the One World database.

"What we're going to do," Patrick explained, "is take a closer look at the eleven companies on your list and rank the ability of each of them to meet every one of your individual criteria, on a scale of one to ten. Then we're going to decide how important each criterion is to you in the 'weight' column—five being most important. The app will multiply rank by weight, total up all the numbers, and voilà: you get a completely objective final score."

"That's brilliant," Jason said.

"It is," Patrick agreed.

Jason looked at his list, then at the list of companies on the screen, then at his wrist at the time. "And we're going to do this . . . for all eleven?"

Patrick nodded. "All of them."

"Do we have time?" Jason asked doubtfully.

"It goes quicker than you think," Patrick said, and nodded at the pen that had—as usual—found its way into Jason's hand. "You got a stylus on the back of that thing?"

Jason glanced at the pen and blinked. "No," he admitted.

Patrick grinned. "Then set it aside, Jaye. We've got work to do."

They ran the numbers on each of Jason's eleven companies as the server brought them drinks, then appetizers, then the main course: a normal-looking Greek salad for Jason, and a bowl of strange-smelling soup for Patrick.

Forty-five minutes later, they had narrowed the eleven companies down to five.

"Which," Patrick concluded, "is a reasonable number to visit."

Jason blinked at him. "Visit?" he repeated.

"Third key of software outsourcing, chief," Patrick reminded him, helping himself to another spoonful of the strange-smelling soup. "In-person investigation is critical."

"Right—about that," Jason started, as the pen slipped back into his hand began tapping itself lightly against the tabletop. "I need an alternative to this 'key.' International travel isn't in the budget. Our CFO will never go for it. I had a hard enough time selling him on the idea of hiring you in the first place." *Also, I'm not good with planes*, he refrained from adding.

"All the CFO's fault, huh?" Patrick said, amused.

Jason stood his ground. "Michael has a bulldog named Cash Flow," he said. "He won't pay for any vet services that exceed the cost of buying a new dog." Granted, the second part was only a less-than-kind rumor around the office—more than likely Ravi's idea of a morbid joke. But Patrick didn't need to know that.

Patrick grew serious for a moment. Or as serious as Patrick got, anyway. "Michael's just going to have to deal with it," he said. "You need to get your butt on a plane."

"Why?" Jason insisted, irked. "We've already established that these people can do the work. Why waste ten days flying all over the place when I can just Skype them and get the interviews over with in ten hours?"

"Because you're not buying a commodity service delivered by nameless, faceless people," Patrick told him without missing a beat.

"You need a team that you can build a good relationship with. Of course, you'll have an initial video call, but if you think that alone is enough for you to make a good decision, you're kidding yourself. You need to see who these people are in a way you'll never get from a video call. How do they live when they're away from the camera? How do they spend their time? How do they work with each other? You don't know."

"I don't need to know," Jason argued. "What I need is developers who can get the job done, and it's clear from these notes that all of these companies can."

Patrick shook his head. "What you need is the ability to collaborate effectively as a team," he said, pointing his soup spoon at Jason for emphasis. "You need to figure out how to communicate, learn each other's strengths and weaknesses. You need to break bread."

Jason groaned. "You're not seriously sending me to the ends of the earth just to have lunch with these people."

"No—I'm sending you to the ends of the earth to bond with these people," Patrick clarified. "Trust me on this. Meeting the people at these companies is critical to selecting the right one. The better you know them, the stronger the glue will be that holds you and your chosen team together, down the road." He slurped down another spoonful of soup. "And while you're down there, you can also verify that everything you found in your preliminary research is actually true. Make sure their company values align with your company values. See for yourself that the people who will be working for you are the kind of people you want on your team."

Jason tapped the pen faster. "I'd like to try just meeting them virtually first," he proposed.

Patrick shrugged. "I can't get on the plane for you. I just hope you have time to start from scratch when your first team falls through, Looney," he said.

For a few seconds, Jason just scowled at him. But they both knew the truth: he didn't have time to make a mistake. "Fine," he muttered, slapping the pen down on the table and crossing his arms. "Have it your way."

Patrick replied with a carefree smile. "Cheers," he said, raising his water glass in the air. He held it aloft until Jason cracked, picked up his own water glass, and completed his half of the toast.

Right . . . cheers, Jason thought. He set his glass down with a sigh and glanced again at his list of finalists: Vietnam, Belarus, Nepal, the Philippines, and Colombia. Jason frowned. "Maybe I'll skip Colombia. I only put it on the list in the first place because it meets all the technical requirements. Since there are four other good options, I think I'll just scratch it off." He took the last bite of his salad and grumbled, "This is going to be scary enough without drug lords, explosions, and murders to worry about."

"What did I tell you about pre-judging countries?" Patrick chided. "Modern-day Colombia isn't anything like that. It's actually beautiful down there. As you will see, firsthand," he finished pointedly, chasing down the statement with another spoonful of stinky soup.

Jason relented with a sigh, and then wrinkled his nose. "What is that, anyway?" he asked.

"İşkembe çorbası? It's tripe," Patrick replied easily. "Here, taste it."

He pushed the bowl toward Jason, and Jason physically recoiled before he could stop himself. All the eyes that had finally gone back to their business swiveled back to their table as Patrick's belly-deep laugh shook the place once more. "Don't be a wuss, kid," Patrick grinned. "When you get to Colombia, you're going to have some *mondongo Colombiano* forced on you at some point, mark my words. May as well get the initiation ceremony over with now."

Because at least here I can throw it up without insulting anyone's national culture? Jason thought. But he steeled himself, took the unused spoon sitting on his napkin, and downed a bite of the stuff like a shot of whiskey.

Patrick gave a whoop and clapped a few times. A smattering of applause went up around them in the restaurant as well, punctuated by giggles. "Here's to your upcoming adventure," Patrick said, getting another spoonful of soup himself and raising it to Jason in a toast before slurping it down. He jerked his chin at the final list of countries. "You ever been to any of these places before?"

Jason shook his head. He felt queasy—whether from the tripe or the prospect of having to drag himself through foreign countries for ten days, it was impossible to say.

Patrick raised an eyebrow. "You ever been *anywhere* before?"

Jason poked at a stray olive on his salad plate. "Does Canada count?" he asked dryly.

Patrick gave another roar of laughter, and this time the applause around the restaurant was directed at him—not that he cared enough to notice. "Chief," he grinned, "trust me: you're in for the time of your life."

NINE

The Decision

"Tell me everything," Paula said.

Jason was holed up in a corner of the buzzing airport in Ho Chi Minh City, Vietnam, waiting to board the plane for the last country on his list—and he'd finally managed to get a hold of her on the Skype phone line for the first time in a week. Not counting the brief emails he'd been sending her every day to let her know that he was still alive, of course.

"Everything?" Jason asked, cracking a small smile. He was jet-lagged and travel weary. Patrick hadn't been kidding when he'd said that Jason was in for the time of his life. "There's a lot of everything."

"I just sat down with dinner and a very large glass of wine," Paula told him. "I've got time."

"I don't," Jason admitted, pressing on his left earbud with his free hand as a bald man with the squeakiest rolling suitcase ever made walked by. "I'm boarding the first plane on my way to Colombia in twenty minutes. What's for dinner?"

"French takeout. I needed it. To drown my sorrows," she said, not very sorrowfully. "You know, from missing you so much." Before he could respond, she added, "Tell me everything that will fit into twenty minutes, then."

So Jason told her.

It had been a battle getting Michael to approve the travel expenses, but he'd won the day in the end with a little support from Scott, and a week later he was touching down in Belarus. Where, as it turned out, they drank a lot of vodka.

"Define 'a lot of vodka,'" Paula said. He heard her take a swig of wine.

"'A lot of vodka' as in you're going to have to test me for liver damage when I get home," Jason defined. "They don't do beer or mixed cocktails. Just large bottles of vodka over a short period of time. During meals, partaking in customs. And apparently it's impolite to sip it; you have to do shots. That's just how they celebrate." Jason winced, remembering the ensuing Belarusian hangover—one for the record books. "They celebrate a lot," he said.

From Belarus, he'd flown to Nepal.

"Patrick gave me this list of things to check on the building tour," he told Paula. "One of them is to make sure the company has an emergency backup energy supply. So I asked them if they had a generator." He pulled his feet underneath his chair as a Vietnamese toddler started running back and forth down the aisle of waiting-room chairs. "They told me to follow them, and we followed this pipe outside to a mystery location—which ended up being a huge barn full of car batteries and a generator. If the electricity goes out, they just crank up the barn."

"You're kidding," Paula said.

"I'm not," Jason laughed. "I actually saw them fire it up during a short power failure. It really works."

The next country on the list had been the Philippines, where he had encountered something even more deadly than vodka.

"What's durian?" Paula asked when he told her its name.

"It's this football-sized, spiky fruit that smells like rotten eggs," Jason explained. "They call it an 'acquired taste.' All I can say is the first person to eat durian must have been really, really hungry." Purely for the sake of not insulting his hosts, he'd tried a durian milkshake that had been barely tolerable. You weren't allowed to ship it on planes. They even had rules against bringing it into the hotel. "I literally saw a sign posted in the lobby that said 'No guns, no prostitutes, no durian,'" he said.

On the other end of the line, he heard Paula choke with laughter on her wine.

And that had brought him here, to Vietnam.

He'd arrived not sure of what to expect, thinking about the destruction of the Vietnam War. But when he checked into his hotel in Da Nang after another redeye flight and looked out the window, the sight had taken him off guard. It was sunrise. People were bathing peacefully in the water on China Beach. Fishermen pushed their boats into the bay and paddled out, serene, as if no one had any memory at all of the violence that had gone on there a few short decades ago—which they probably didn't, because the majority of the current population had been born after the war.

"The real danger was crossing the street," Jason confided.

"Come again?" Paula asked.

"I'm in Ho Chi Minh City," said Jason. "The roads are packed, 99 percent of the vehicles there are mopeds, and they hardly have any crosswalk signals or traffic lights." The airline attendant at the flight desk called the group boarding number on his ticket—first, for once—and Jason rose and headed to the gate, careful to swerve around the still-sprinting toddler as he continued talking to Paula. "You just cross the street wherever, and the traffic flows around you—like water around a rock."

Paula scoffed. "And you lived to tell the tale, huh?"

"Amazingly enough," Jason confirmed, letting the attendant tear his ticket and continuing down the boarding ramp. "It makes no sense, but if you walk slowly and steadily, the mopeds somehow miss you. Anyway, honey, listen, I'm going to have to go in a minute. The plane is boarding."

"Fine," she sighed. "Just leave me to cry into my lonely escargots. Where are you going in Colombia again?"

"Medellín," he reminded her, adding as he stretched his sore neck, "which will make four continents in ten days, if you include the one we live on."

At the other end of the line, he heard Paula snort and realized she was laughing. "What?" he asked.

"All this time I've been trying to fight my way into Doctors Without Borders," she said. "You just got dragged into Software Without Borders. It's not fair."

Jason smiled. Not a single day of his international road trip had been comfortable. But he couldn't deny that, for a self-described antisocial developer, he'd gotten more out of it than he'd thought he would, so far. "Love you," he told Paula. "Drink an extra glass of wine for me."

"Love you too," she said. "Email me when you get to Medellín."

"I will," Jason promised.

After he hung up, Jason stowed his carry-on, settled into his seat by the window, and closed his eyes, letting his head fall back on the headrest. It was a twenty-six-hour trip to Colombia—and he intended to sleep through every minute of it.

⸻

Twenty-eight hours later, Jason was standing on a tree-lined avenue in Colombia, gazing up at the four-story, off-white plaster building that housed MedellínTech.

The company's head of business development, Ramón, had personally picked him up at the Rionegro airport. Jason had already met Ramón a few times via Skype, and liked him: he was a thin man with short dark hair, and friendly enough, but what Jason appreciated most about him were the sharp eyes that came with the smile. Ramón was 110 percent on top of things. Jason had yet to see one small detail slip through the cracks in their correspondence.

"Welcome to Colombia," Ramón said warmly when he shook Jason's hand at the gate. "I hope you're not afraid of heights."

Jason wasn't. But the drive from the plateau where the airport was located down into the valley almost changed his mind.

Colombia was green and mountainous, with tortuous roads winding in and around the mountains, sometimes at steep angles. Jason stared out the window as they made their way down the highway from the airport, unable to look away from the incredible view of the city below. Ramón kept up an easy conversation about Jason's trip, ShapeShift, and life in California as they went.

Halfway down the mountain, Ramón pulled over at a tiny restaurant called Rosa's Café, where he insisted on treating Jason to *mondongo Colombiano*—just as Patrick had predicted. What Patrick had failed to mention, however, was that tripe stew made in Colombia tasted about a thousand times better than its Californian counterpart. He drained the dregs of it while Ramón looked on with approval.

All told, not including the stop for lunch, the drive into Medellín had taken about an hour. When they finally arrived, Ramón had dropped Jason off in front of the building while he went to park the car. Where he planned to park it, Jason couldn't guess. He hadn't noticed any parking lots on the drive in. As far as he could see down the boulevard, people walked and rode bikes, wandering in and out of pastry shops for coffee on their way to or from lunch.

Ramón appeared among the pedestrians just a minute or two after dropping Jason off and caught up with him on the sidewalk in front of the building. "Shall we go in?" he asked, and Jason nodded.

MedellínTech's head of business development led the way through the double front doors, swiping an identification card to gain access. As Jason followed, he caught sight of a sign posted on the wall next to the entrance:

> **Developers: You are now entering an English-only zone**

Impressive, he thought. That boded well for communication.

The sharp-looking woman manning the front desk smiled at him as he passed her, and an armed security guard posted between her desk and the elevator gave him a nod. Ramón called the elevator and, once they were inside, hit the button for the first floor.

I'm never going to get used to that, Jason thought as they lurched up to what he considered to be the second floor of the building. The "first floor" of the countries he'd visited in Europe and Asia had been his equivalent of level two as well.

The doors dinged open, and Ramón struck out across a bright sea of modern blue cubicles paired with blue chairs. Pops of red and orange accented the walls. Most people worked diligently, some leaning over the low walls of the cubicles to puzzle out problems together. One woman with her back to Jason hummed the *Titanic* theme song as she plugged away at her keyboard. The few people who noticed him walking by smiled and gave him small waves— even, once, a little salute. He returned the greetings, slightly self-conscious, but grateful for the warm welcome nonetheless.

"After you," Ramón said, pushing the door to a conference room open for Jason and stepping out of the way.

"Thanks." Jason smiled at him and walked in.

A stocky man with thick black hair turned to greet him as he entered. "Jason," he said boisterously, his accent round and heavy, dragging out the "jay" in Jason's name. He crossed the room in a few strides and shook Jason's hand with enthusiasm—like a good-natured bear. "Welcome to Colombia!" he grinned. "I am Hector Gonzalez, CEO of MedellínTech."

"Great to meet you," Jason said, discreetly regaining his balance as Hector released his hand.

"Come in, come in, sit down. How was the drive down the mountain, eh?" Hector ushered him to a seat at the conference table. Before Jason could answer the question, the CEO went on. "We have fruit for you!" he announced, sweeping his hand toward a spread of bananas, sliced mangoes and pineapples, and another orange offering that Jason didn't recognize. "Pastries too, from Valentina's—best bakery in Medellín. And coffee, but it is not so good. All the good coffee, they send it to America." He laughed, a brash peal of a sound that reverberated in the walls—like Patrick's long-lost Colombian cousin.

Jason laughed along and helped himself to the coffee. Hector was right: it was just okay. "Could I get the WiFi password from you really quick?" he said, opening his laptop. "I just need to let my wife know that I made it safe."

"Of course, of course," Hector obliged, and scrawled a tongue twister of a Spanish word—barricaded by numbers and symbols—on a scrap of paper for Jason to copy. Jason logged on long enough to shoot a quick aliveness report to Paula. Then he turned his attention back to Hector, who beckoned him to the wall-to-wall window on the far side of the room. "Come," he grinned. "The rest are arriving soon—you are early. Come see where you have come from."

Jason joined him at the window, toting his unexceptional coffee with him.

The view was as spectacular looking up as it had been looking down. He let Hector tell him about the history of the city while he stared at the buildings rolling away across the basin of the valley, then up at the skyscrapers built into the hills. "How do they do that?" Jason asked with a nod at the skyscrapers, when the CEO finally paused long enough to let him get a word in edgewise.

Hector laughed his roaring laugh and slapped Jason on the back, as if congratulating the funny American on a particularly good joke. Jason barely kept the coffee in his cup from sloshing over. "Jason," he said, "here we are software developers, not architects. Who knows how they build these crazy things?"

At that moment, the door to the conference room opened, and four Colombians filed in, chatting loudly with one another—two women and two men. Hector introduced each of them as they approached Jason to say hello, greeting him like a long-lost brother. "Andrés, Jason. Andrés, he is our project management director, okay? Camilla, our HR leader, yes. Luis, the QA director, and here is Almendra, the scrum master." Jason navigated the flurry of handshakes, shoulder slaps, and even a hug from Almendra as they converged on him one after the next, smiling and showering him with words of welcome.

Then Hector clapped his hands twice, and the din died down. "We begin!" he declared.

Everyone took their seats, leaving the one with the best view of the presentation screen for Jason. The presentations took about two hours, all told. But for Jason, the time flew by.

They were fantastic.

He took notes on all of them, just as he'd done in the other countries. Hector went first, giving a ten-minute value proposition, sharing MedellínTech's core values (an almost perfect match to ShapeShift's), and recounting a brief history of the company. They had started out as a basic software development company fifteen years ago, but had done so poorly that Hector realized they were going to need to study procedures to become a solid organization.

"Otherwise, we were going to spend the rest of our lives fixing bugs!" he said, and the rest of the group joined in with his rumbling laugh. He explained the custom software processes they'd come up with for the business, all of which had launched them to success in the global marketplace. Jason nodded along as he jotted down notes, impressed:

- Knows pure Agile & scrum
- Uses coding standards and code reviews
- Uses design & architecture patterns
- Certifications: CMMi level 5, ISO 9001, ISO 27001
- International Award for Software Excellence

Andrés, the PMO, followed Hector's act by introducing his process for overseeing the team. Again, Jason made notes:

- Field error rate 12 orders of magnitude lower than average
- JEE technology stack = exceptional productivity
- Agile, test-driven development
- 12–14 ELOC per hour

The HR leader, Camilla, explained MedellínTech's hiring process—which seemed designed from start to finish to strain talented, passionate coders from the rabble.

- 400+ employees
- Attrition rate = 6.0%, voluntary and involuntary (lowest in industry)

The QA director, Luis, went next. Every word that came out of his mouth was like music to Jason's ears as the man described their quality assurance processes, the metrics used to measure team performance, and the tools used to manage development—including the burndown chart for each sprint. Luis described their methods for managing software control and how they pulled off test-driven development.

This is even better than what we do at ShapeShift, Jason thought, impressed. *They actually do continuous integration and deployment.*

He himself had been thinking about implementing continuous deployment for months, but it was hardly for the faint of heart. MedellínTech was looking better by the minute.

Almendra, the scrum master, gave her presentation last. For all that she clearly had a good head on her shoulders, everything about her was warm and friendly, from her voice, to the laugh lines at the corners of her eyes, to the long brown hair tied into a messy bun at the nape of her neck. She wore a red shirt with the word "Bazinga!" emblazoned across the chest.

Wow, that's a real word in Spanish? Jason thought. *I thought Sheldon from* The Big Bang Theory *made it up.* He made a note to ask Almendra what it meant later, in addition to his regular notes:

- Application development: Java, JavaScript, HTML5, CSS3, JEE, C++, PHP
- Databases: Cassandra, MongoDB (NoSQL) MySQL, Oracle SQL Server (RDBMS),
- Methodologies: Agile (SCRUM, XP), Kanban, SOA

After the presentations ended, the team leaders threw Jason back to Ramón for the building tour. He heard Hector on the phone behind them as they left the conference room, telling someone to make reservations for four tonight at . . . his words changed from English to Spanish as the door closed.

Almendra accompanied Jason and Ramón to the elevator, since her office was on the next floor. Jason seized his opportunity. "What does 'bazinga' mean?" he asked as the metal doors closed behind the three of them.

She raised her eyebrows at him. "It's from *The Big Bang Theory.* Sheldon says it," she laughed, adding her best impersonation for emphasis: *"Bazinga!* My sister and I went to a U2 concert in Boston last month. I saw it in a shop and could not resist." The elevator doors opened on her floor. "Enjoy your tour!" she called with a cheerful wave back at him, walking off the elevator.

Jason waved back, speechless. *A U2 concert? Really?*

Ramón crossed his arms and tutted at Jason as the doors closed and the elevator lurched upward again. "You have never heard of 'bazinga'?" he shook his head in mock disappointment. "You must be a bad American."

"No," Jason gave him a rueful smile. "Just a bad Spanish speaker."

They toured the building from top to bottom.

It was a nice place—both by Colombian standards and by Jason's personal ones. ("Don't judge the workspace based on what you're used to," Patrick had warned him before he left. "Judge it by the standards of the country you're in. The company might be in a house, but a house is a perfectly professional place to run a company in some parts of the world." The company Jason had visited in Vietnam had, in fact, been located in a venerable-looking Victorian.) Everywhere they went, the same open feeling of collaboration and enjoyment that Jason had seen on the "first" floor ran rampant.

They also passed plenty of soundproof rooms guarded by doors with security access codes. *Intellectual privacy protection: check*, Jason thought. All the technical safety measures on Patrick's list seemed to be in place.

Jason did have to sigh when he visited the restroom and saw the small trashcan sitting next to the toilet. Another "no flush" situation with the toilet paper. That had been a theme throughout his travels, in general.

Sunset was closing in by the time they finished the tour.

"I will drive you to your hotel . . ." Ramón started.

Yes, Jason thought. *Please.* All he wanted, in the entire world, was a pillow and ten hours of non-vertical, uninterrupted sleep.

". . . and after you have settled in, we will meet the others for a meal."

Jason smothered the groan that bubbled up from the depths of his ribcage by sheer force of will. "Sounds great," he said.

The hotel was less than ten minutes away, by car. Ramón parked out front and dropped him off. "Have a rest," he said generously. "In thirty minutes, I will come back and get you for supper." Then he smiled and, Jason imagined, drove off to find another invisible parking place to wait.

Supper was served at Restaurante Carmen—a little eatery holed up in a traditional house with a thatched roof, complete with quaint décor, a mosaic-tiled floor, wooden beams, and interesting religious imagery brandished across the walls.

"*Aguardiente*," Hector jovially commanded the waitress as soon as they sat down. "For the table."

Jason suppressed a groan. He knew only one thing about *aguardiente*, and that was that its makeup consisted of anywhere from 30 to 60 percent alcohol. It didn't help that he was jetlagged and dehydrated from all the traveling. *This might give the Belarusians a run for their money*, he thought grimly.

They had put him next to Hector at the thick, square wooden table, with Almendra across from Jason and Ramón seated next to her. "Andrés is sending his apologies," Hector said, pouring Jason the first shot of *aguardiente* as soon as the waitress set the squat bottle of clear liquid on their table, along with four bright ceramic shot glasses. After Jason had been served, Hector passed shots around to the others as well. "He wanted to come, but tonight his grandmother has ninety years old," he explained.

"*Is* ninety years old," Almendra clucked, leaning across the table and swatting Hector lightly on the arm.

"Yes, this is what I said. She is ninety years old," Hector defended himself. "So tonight he celebrates her with his family. And we celebrate you," he chuckled, raising his shot glass. "Salud!"

"Salud!" echoed Ramón and Almendra, and Jason managed a smile as he mumbled along with the toast and raised his glass as well. *Here goes nothing*, he thought, downing the shot.

It was sweeter than vodka, he decided, trying not to be too obvious as he gasped for air. But they definitely didn't call it "fire water" for nothing.

Hector laughed his roar of a laugh, pounded Jason on the back, and served him another shot. Thankfully, Jason was spared from having to drink it right away by the reappearance of the waitress, come to take their orders.

Jason did his best to keep up with the flurry of Spanish for the appetizers that Ramón, Almendra, and Hector all seemed to order at once, though the only thing he caught for sure was when Hector lapsed into English and declared with a grin, "Pizza for the *Americano*! Corn and avocado *por favor, señora.*"

Jason was grateful that he already knew what he wanted when the waitress went around and asked them for their individual main courses.

"I'd like the *mondongo Colombiano*," he said, and the eruption of whoops, clapping, and appreciative laughter from around the table almost knocked him out of his chair. Even the waitress smiled.

"The gringo is one of us!" Hector announced, and raised another toast, which Almendra and Ramón downed with gusto. Jason followed suit. He could already feel a pleasant buzz in his bones. Before the waitress slipped away to put in their order, he heard Hector ask for another bottle of *aguardiente*.

"What news of Manuel, Hector?" Almendra asked when the waitress had gone.

Hector shook his head. "No better, no worse," he said. Then he turned to Jason to explain. "My brother, he is getting a divorce." He chuckled. "His wife is a divorce lawyer. This is the irony. He is no lucky."

"*Not* lucky," tutted Almendra.

"What? I said this. He is not lucky," Hector retorted. Then he sighed, a sound almost as belly deep as his laugh. Two fingers turned his shot glass on the table. Beneath their thick brows, his eyes were somber. "It is a shame, this," he said. "Shame, to split the family."

"I'm sorry," Jason said, and found that he really meant it.

"You have a large family?" Ramón asked him.

Jason shook his head. "No. They live on the other side of the country. I only see them once a year, for the holidays."

"Once a *year*?" Almendra's eyes were huge with disbelief.

Jason nodded. He was vaguely aware that he ought to feel self-conscious at her shock, but sheer exhaustion and the *aguardiente* seemed to have broken his embarrassment mechanism. He liked the feeling. *Maybe I can smuggle some of this stuff home in my suitcase*, he thought. "Do you see your family often?" he asked Almendra.

She laughed, and both Hector and Ramón smiled along with her. "Here, yes. Every day, almost every day," she explained. "In Colombia, family—it is everything, everything."

Then she told a story about how, when she was growing up, her parents had been too poor to put her and her six siblings through college. So the entire family scrimped, saved, and supported to get the eldest sibling—a brother—through school. Once he graduated, that brother paid for the education of the second-oldest sibling. The second oldest then paid the way of the third oldest, and so on until all seven Sanchez children had graduated with advanced degrees.

"Now we take care of our parents," Almendra concluded. "They have everything they want. But they always say, 'To have the family together, that is enough for us.'"

"That's incredible," Jason said. Somewhere over the course of the story, he'd leaned into the table to hear her better, his elbow braced on the tabletop and his chin propped on his knuckles. He made no objection when Hector slid another shot of *aguardiente* in front of him. Inspired, he raised the glass himself. "To family," he said.

"To family," the Colombians echoed, and another round of fire water disappeared.

The food arrived, and it was worth being dragged out of his hotel room for, Jason decided. More than worth it. The *mondongo Colombiano* came close to putting the bowl he'd had at Rosa's Café to shame.

The Colombians approved of his gusto in devouring it.

"You do not have passion, you do not live," Hector declared. "Everything, you must do with passion. Eat with passion. Drink with passion. Love with passion. Code with passion. This is the Colombian way."

"You always eat with passion, Hector," Ramón joked.

"What can I say?" Hector grinned. "Always my mother tells me, I am a healthy appetite."

"You *have* a healthy appetite," Almendra corrected.

"Yes, I said this. I have a healthy appetite."

And suddenly—blame it on the *aguardiente*—Jason got it. He understood what had been happening to him, not just in this country, but in all the others as well.

He'd left California with the idea that he was going on a business trip, steeling himself for days of small talk and forced, stiff socializing with strangers. But in almost every scenario he'd been through in the past ten days, one key part of that equation had been missing: the strangers.

This trip had pushed him headlong out of his comfort zone, personally as well as professionally. And, to his own amazement, he was loving it.

Patrick had been right. These people were more than business transactions. They felt like new team members. More than that, they felt like friends.

You win, Delaney, he thought as the Colombians started trying to force each other to take the leftovers home to their respective families. *I'm glad I got my butt on a plane.*

⁕ ⋯⋯⋯ ⁕

The next day flew by.

Jason spent a little more time with the leadership in the morning, getting the lowdown on the specifics of the software development process, as well as the systems in place for facilitating communication challenges and addressing cultural sensitivity. He confirmed that MedellínTech had recently worked on applications like the ones he needed to build for BurnRate, and he learned that all of them had top-notch development experience themselves.

But he spent the bulk of his time interviewing his potential team.

His technical leader, should he decide to go with MedellínTech, was a tall, thin man by the name of Sebastián. Sebastián was a little reserved for a Colombian, and didn't talk much. Nonetheless, it only took about twenty minutes going over some of the code he'd done for other clients to see that he was a genius. Jason would be lucky to have him on his side.

The award for the most colorful interview with a developer went to one Marco Perez.

"Marco?" Jason had asked, holding out his hand as Marco entered the conference room that was serving as Jason's base camp for the visit.

"Polo!" Marco responded with shameless enthusiasm, and erupted into a fit of laughter so genuine that he could barely manage the handshake. "A joke! One of our Italian clients taught it to me," he explained, grinning ear to ear.

You're going to get along really well with Ravi, Jason thought.

He asked Marco the same questions he'd asked the other developers: What kind of software technologies have you used in the past? What kind of testing processes and methodologies are you using now? What trends are you watching? He also asked Marco to describe the company's software development process. As with the other developers, Marco's version checked out against what Andrés and Almendra had described to him earlier.

Almost before he knew it, Jason was saying his farewells.

"Well, Jason, I have a pleasure to meet you," Hector said with another bear-like handshake.

"It *was* a pleasure to meet you," Almendra agreed. Behind her, Sebastián and Andrés nodded. "Safe travels back to California," she said, as the laugh lines at the corners of her eyes crinkled in a smile.

"Maybe we see you soon for some more *mondongo Colombiano!*" Hector grinned.

"I wouldn't miss it," Jason laughed, adding one of the Spanish phrases he'd picked up during the visit: "¡*Mucho gusto!*"

A few more goodbye handshakes and he was in Ramón's car again, driving up and out of the valley . . . past the skyscrapers built into the hillsides . . . past Rosa's Café, where they had stopped for lunch his first day . . . and, finally, up to the Rionegro airport.

"Thanks for everything," Jason told his host, giving Ramón a sincere handshake. "I'll be in touch."

"You're very welcome," Ramón replied warmly. "I look forward to hearing from you."

An hour later, Jason was on his way home.

At first, he tried to sleep. He'd gotten progressively better at sleeping on planes since this trip had begun, and he had high hopes for the fourteen-hour journey home in particular. Every cell in his body was screaming for rest.

Unfortunately, every neuron in his brain was likewise screaming for analysis.

After half an hour of restless tossing, the neurons won the raging internal battle for his attention. Jason groaned softly, ordered a double espresso from the in-flight virtual snack bar, and opened his laptop. He pulled up Patrick's checklist for the fourth key of software outsourcing—"Quality matters as much as price"—and hunkered down to comb through his extensive notes.

Even with Patrick's guidelines, the decision wasn't easy.

Every company he'd interviewed had been pretty terrific, with one exception: the team in the Philippines that ShapeShift's VC had referred him to. Jason had visited two Philippine companies, and the one from Patrick's database was excellent: great people, nice atmosphere, amazing qualifications.

The VC's company, even though it was just across town, had seemed like a different world.

It felt like a factory. Everyone worked with their heads down, never looking up, never speaking to one another—let alone collaborating. They were clearly more interested in having stable careers than they were in doing work they loved. The building was run-down by Philippine standards. They didn't have air conditioning in the server room, which was outdated to begin with, and it must've been 120 degrees in there. Worst of all, the senior management had no sense of what it meant to be an engineer, solving problems. At one point, the CEO had actually said to Jason, verbatim, "We're at the cutting edge and really getting into cloud enablement." Whatever that meant.

The one thing they had going for them was much cheaper fees.

Well, that gives me a head start, anyway, Jason thought, crossing them off the list. He didn't even need to reference Patrick's matrix.

Which was good, because the rest of the decision-making process was going to be torture.

All of the other companies had been pretty incredible, and each of them had a different edge. The Belarusian company in Minsk, for example, had a morning standup with sixty people in the same room, all of them talking about the challenges they were having and their engagement with their individual clients. Short as it was, the cross-pollination, collaboration, and innovation were obvious.

And that was only the beginning.

Jason hunkered down in his seat and began the tedious process of combing through all of his notes.

Hours of deliberation went by. One company fell by the wayside. Then another. The defeated sleep-craving body cells launched a surprise revolt after all, and he jolted awake an hour or two later with a dent in the side of his forehead from where he'd drifted off on top of the pen he'd been holding. He rubbed it with the heel of his hand and got back to work.

Finally, when the flight map showed that they were less than an hour away from landing, he came to a decision.

The elation combined with the longstanding lack of sleep was like downing an entire bottle of *aguardiente* in five minutes. Jason was almost delirious enough to imagine that he might be able to buoy the altitude of the plane by an extra hundred feet by force of sheer triumph.

On a high, he connected to the plane's WiFi and shot Patrick an email with the news of his decision—along with the foolproof list of reasons that had helped him make it.

It was about nine o'clock in the morning, California time. Patrick responded to his message within minutes.

"Great choice. You did good, chief," he wrote.

"Thanks," Jason typed back. Before hitting send, he allowed himself a smug smile and added, "P.S.—The *mondongo Colombiano* was delicious."

Then he snapped the laptop shut, leaned his head back against the seat, and allowed himself a sigh of relief. He had scoured every last doubt from his mind: MedellínTech was the best partner for ShapeShift, even though they cost more than the Asian options. In spite of all odds *and* the curse of Rick Looney hanging over his head, he was making positive progress. He closed his eyes and smiled.

I've found our outsourcing team.

TEN

We Need a Toyota

o way are we hiring this company in Colombia."

Jason was back in the glass-walled conference room at ShapeShift, standing at one end of the long table as he presented the findings of his trip to the leadership. Michael sat to the left of him, the look on his face an eerily good imitation of Cash Flow the bulldog's. Behind him, Lance leaned back in his chair, silent and distant. Scott, at the other end of the table, was back in freight-train mode, fingers steepled and brow lowered as his eyes bored holes through Jason's own. Lisbeth sat around the corner from him on the right side of the table, eyebrows furrowed, two fingers pressed over her mouth in concentration.

Jason resisted the urge to reach for the pen in his shirt pocket. For a moment there, back on the plane, he'd enjoyed such a nice delusion that everyone on the executive team would welcome his decision with open arms.

Clearly, he'd had a little too much *aguardiente* before leaving Medellín.

"Look at these numbers," Michael went on, waving a disgusted hand at Jason's digital report on his tablet as though they were a personal insult. "You want to pay 50 percent more for Colombia to do the same work we can have done in the Philippines at a fraction of the cost? Are you trying to sink us?"

Biting down a sarcastic retort, Jason managed evenly, "Of course not." He looked at Scott.

"I'm under pressure from the VCs to go with the Philippine company they suggested," the CEO told Jason. Despite the intensity of his gaze, the words were neutral.

"Because they don't want to see their money wasted on stunts like this," Michael said, and this time the disgusted hand wave was directed at Jason himself. "We never should have sent him on that trip. What a waste."

"You approved the travel budget," Lisbeth pointed out.

"They overruled me," Michael retorted, glaring between Jason and Scott. "And now he"—this with a jerk of his stout chin in Jason's direction—"wants to sign us up for this circus at a *50 percent higher rate* than we actually need to pay?" He set his mouth in an unbreakable line. "I'm not having it."

Jason looked down at the table for a moment and silently counted to five, letting the wave of frustration that rolled through him die back down to a simmer. *Three weeks ago, I didn't get it either,* he coached himself. *Just explain how it works.* He stole a glance at the wall of pigheadedness that was Michael and inhaled a deep breath. *Slowly,* he added.

Jason had one thing going for him: after the fourteen-hour flight home from Medellín, every last guideline of Patrick's fourth key of software outsourcing—"Quality matters as much as price"—was ingrained in his mental arsenal of logic.

He pulled the first one out.

"You can't go off of the bottom line alone. You have to look at what you're getting for your money," Jason explained. "The VC's Philippine company cuts some dangerous corners. I saw it. I was there. Their equipment is shoddy; even the building itself is in disrepair. They charge less because they're dodging basic overhead costs and hiring cheap, unhappy developers. That translates into a huge risk on our part, if we decide to work with them.

"The extra 50 percent MedellínTech charges isn't arbitrary," he went on. "It's paying for a better-quality team. Good tools, good work conditions, and especially good people."

"Code is code," Michael growled. "What does it matter who produces it?"

Maybe that rumor about the dog and vet bills is actually true, Jason thought grimly. "Look, I know it sounds counterintuitive, but quality isn't really about technical skill and experience at the end of the day," he said. "The quality we need for BurnRate is going to come from having a team we can collaborate and communicate with well. We need EQ as much as we need IQ—maybe even more—and we get that with the Colombians. Again," he added pointedly, "I've met these people. I've seen their hiring standards. I've seen how they work. Their company culture and values are a dead ringer for ShapeShift's."

"You're trying to sell us on a Ferrari," Michael accused. "All we need here is a Yugo. Something that will get us from point A to point B."

"I'm not trying to sell you a Ferrari," Jason said, irritation prickling at the back of his neck. "I'm trying to show you that we don't need a Ferrari *or* a Yugo. We need a Toyota: a solid team at a stable company, with years and thousands of hours of experience, that's low maintenance as well as cost effective. We need a track record of consistency." *Not to mention continuous improvement,* he added to himself. "*That's* what's going to get us from point A to point B. If we buy the Yugo, we're just going to end up spending a fortune in money *and* lost time on repairs—and it'll end up costing more than if we'd just bought the Toyota in the first place." He paused to catch his breath before he went on. "MedellínTech is our Toyota. We have to strike a balance between talent and cost."

Michael snorted. "You pick the second most expensive company on the list and call it 'balance'?"

"In this case, yes," Jason insisted. "You're after an attractive price tag, but I'm telling you, it'll come back to bite us in the end. You can't get the same level of coding done for half the price. You have to factor in communication challenges, time zone differences—there's a whole list. But the bottom line is, this isn't rocket science. Quality people produce quality software. For everything the Colombian team offers us, it's a fair price. More than fair. Some of these people are smarter than we are."

"Which is expensive," Michael scowled.

"Which is how we build an excellent company," Jason retorted. "Look," he said, addressing the table at large, "we're in this mess in the first place because we didn't push the envelope enough. We need a team that will help us think outside the box, before the box collapses on us."

Michael set his jaw. "We need to stay in budget, is what we need."

"I agree," Jason told him, exasperation finally breaking into his voice. "We also need to get BurnRate to market fast, so that we can capture revenue and market share sooner, so that we can create a beachhead around our product in a competitive marketplace. Only the *right* team will make that happen for us, Michael." He sighed. "Look, we're saving a lot of money by outsourcing in the first place. At the end of the day, we don't just need 'faster and cheaper.' We need a quality product that will reestablish us as leaders in the marketplace. That's where the sustainable revenue stream will come from." He turned away from Michael and looked Scott in the eye. "I guarantee you that we will *not* have the quality product we need if we go with the VC's team in the Philippines."

Michael grumbled something under his breath but, finally, fell quiet. Scott stared intently at Jason over his steepled fingers. For once, Jason didn't back down. The silence around them seemed to stretch for miles.

Then, finally, Lisbeth cleared her throat.

"We just spent two weeks and thousands of dollars sending Jason around the world to meet these companies," she pointed out. "He's working with a coach who knows a lot more about outsourcing software development than we do. I think it's time to admit that we don't know what we don't know and let Jason do this the way he thinks it needs to be done."

Another tense silence. Jason held his breath.

Then Michael gave one last scowl and nodded. Lance said nothing, which was as good as acquiescence. Lisbeth's face was all stubborn conviction.

Scott looked around the table, then back at Jason. His huge shoulders heaved a slow sigh. Then he took down his steepled fingers and folded his hands. "All right," he said. "Hire the Colombian team. I'll deal with the objections from the VCs." A little of the freight-train-intensity focus crept back into his eyes before he dismissed the meeting. "I hope you know what you're doing, Jaye."

Me too, Jason thought as they all gathered their things and filed out of the conference room. He expelled a long breath. *Here goes nothing.*

ELEVEN

Connecting

I t's official. We just hired the Colombians."

Jason had been trying to get a hold of Patrick all morning. So, of course, Patrick had chosen to call him back exactly five minutes before the virtual meeting Jason had scheduled to introduce the onsite team to their new MedellínTech partners.

"Terrific! You're on your way." He could practically hear Patrick's lazy grin through the phone. "Literally, by the sound of it. Where are you headed?"

Jason's pen slipped out of his shirt pocket as he bent to pick up his laptop case from where it had fallen on the floor beside his desk. He grumbled a curse under his breath as he snatched it back up, stuffed the laptop into the case, and strode out of his office. "I'm about to introduce my team to the Colombians," he said.

"Good idea," Patrick approved.

"Your idea," Jason pointed out.

"I do have good ideas," Patrick mused.

Jason rolled his eyes. "Look," he said, "I only have a minute. Any words of wisdom before ShapeShift and Colombia collide?"

"Just remind your team not to get hung up on the superficial stuff. Be flexible with the cultural differences. Should be a cinch.

You guys are all shapeshifters over there, right?" He laughed his devil-may-care, booming laugh.

"What would I do without you?" Jason asked dryly.

"I shudder to think, Looney," Patrick chuckled. "Go knock 'em dead."

"Thanks."

"*Hasta luego.*"

Jason hung up the phone and speed-walked the rest of the way to the meeting.

Ravi, Marion, and the rest of the development team were already assembled in the "war room"—so dubbed by Ravi because it was one of the few spaces in the office without at least one glass wall. Lance was missing, Jason noticed with a frown; he'd asked him to put in an appearance on behalf of the image processing team. But there was no time to track him down now.

"All right," Jason said to the room. "Let's do this."

"We can't," Ravi told him.

"What? Why?" Jason's heart sank. *Not another omen.* "Is Skype down?"

"No, Skype's fine," said Ravi, brow furrowed as he hunched over a laptop hooked up to the much larger screen that dominated the meeting room. "I can't get the camera to connect."

"You already rebooted?" Jason asked.

"Who am I, your eighty-year-old mother?" Ravi replied. "Of course I rebooted." Marion was bent over the computer with him, her standard frown of concern even deeper than usual.

Jason sighed and dug his own laptop out of its case. "Here," he said, "let's hook mine up instead and see if it helps."

A couple minutes later, the video was up and running. Jason saw Lance quietly let himself into the war room—where he stood against the back wall with his arms folded and no expression on his face—a split second before Skype connected with Medellín and a smiling Almendra filled the screen.

"You made it!" she laughed.

"We got stuck in traffic," Ravi grinned. Within seconds, it was clear that he was going to get along with the fun-loving Colombians just fine.

Not including the hiccup with the camera, the introductions went fairly well. A few of the onsite developers were taken off guard by the boisterous familiarity of their MedellínTech counterparts, but most acclimated quickly. *True shapeshifters*, Jason thought in spite of himself, and then rolled his eyes. *Darn you, Delaney.*

Marion proved to be the biggest stumbling block.

"You are the product owner?" Almendra had grinned when Jason introduced the two of them. "I am the scrum master. You and I will be best friends by the end of the week, eh?" she laughed.

"I'm pleased to meet you," Marion had responded, with a reserved nod.

Almendra had cocked her head slightly and laughed again, as though trying to decide whether Marion's formality was intended as a joke.

Fortunately, Ravi's good humor was enough to put the whole of the Colombian team at ease. He cracked a joke or two when Almendra introduced him to Sebastián, and even MedellínTech's taciturn technical leader had to smile in spite of himself.

Then Jason introduced Marco.

"Everyone," he said to the ShapeShift team at large, "I'd like you to meet Marco—"

"Polo!"

For a moment it sounded like an echo over the line. But in the beat of silence that followed, Jason noted the matching looks of surprise on Marco and Ravi's faces before the two of them simultaneously burst into hopeless laughter. They had both delivered the punch line at the same time.

Love at first sight, Jason thought wryly as the two men got over their laughing fit and started bantering back and forth, exchanging an air high five.

By the time the meeting disbanded forty-five minutes later, he felt satisfied that the basics had been settled. Everyone knew who was responsible for what and who their main touch points of communication were. ShapeShift would have continuous access to a copy of the source code that the Colombians would be working on through GitHub. Ravi and Marion had appointments with Sebastián and Almendra, respectively, to communicate the more specific details of what needed to be done for sprint zero. Lance slipped out the door again before Jason could discuss first impressions with him, but at least he'd been present for the meeting. Jason would get his thoughts later.

As he collected his laptop and headed back to his office, Jason caught himself feeling cautiously optimistic. *Maybe this insane idea actually stands a chance of working out,* he thought.

TWELVE

Putting Out Fires

Then again, maybe the idea of software outsourcing "working out" was as crazy as it had sounded from day one.

No one had a word to say against the quality of the Colombians' work, itself. They were outstanding developers, and they produced beautiful code.

However, three sprints into the project, the practical logistics of working with a team on another continent were presenting a few challenges.

For starters, Medellín was two hours ahead of Mountain View. It didn't sound like much. In fact, the large overlap between the ShapeShift and MedellínTech workdays had been one of the reasons Jason chose the Colombians in the first place. What difference did a couple of hours make?

He found out firsthand the first time the ShapeShift team held its standard end-of-day recap meeting, after the Colombians were on board.

"All right, where do we stand with including microservices updates in our continuous build process?" Marion asked, running down her checklist.

"Marco was handling it," Ravi told her.

"Well, is he still handling it or has it been handled?" Marion pressed. "We can't do a reliable production build until we know."

"I'll ask him in the morning," said Ravi. "Everyone in Medellín has already gone home for the day."

"We can't ask him in the morning," Marion frowned at her list. "We need to know now. If he's done with it, we have to send him instructions for adding in the new microservices for the image recognition features that Lance's team is working on. Otherwise he's going to waste two hours twiddling his thumbs in the morning."

Mornings were another thing.

Marion wasn't far off the mark in her fears that the Colombian team would be left twiddling their thumbs. More often than Jason liked, the ShapeShift team arrived at the office to find important questions from the offshore developers waiting for them—questions that the Colombians needed answers to before they could move forward. Every time it happened, it meant two more hours of progress down the drain.

The lost hours were starting to add up to delayed results. They'd missed a key UI feature on the mobile application in the first sprint because of it, and had failed to add the ability for users to edit their nutrition history in the second one.

Nor was the time difference the only thing causing delays.

It turned out that the Colombians' technical leader, Sebastián, wasn't just taciturn because he was introverted, as Jason had first assumed. He also didn't talk much because his English wasn't the best. The man really was a genius, but miscommunications were slipping through the cracks as a result of the language barrier, which was causing some problems with the process. Which meant they were having to go back and fix things. Which meant that progress wasn't coming along as quickly as Jason had hoped it would.

. . . which didn't sit well with the ShapeShift executive team.

"The VCs are breathing down my neck, Jaye," Scott had told him a few days ago. "You've got to give me more than this to show them."

"I know," Jason had said. "I'll see what I can do."

In the developers' defense, however, the executive team didn't have the most realistic expectations for how onboarding the new outsourcers would work. They thought the Colombian team should be able to hit the ground running.

"It doesn't work that way," Jason had ranted to Paula one night over French takeout. ("We need it," she'd said. "To relieve your stress.") "You don't just pick up someone else's code the way you pick up a book. You have to learn how it works. Get up to speed on it before you can use it productively."

"You're right. It's tragic, honey. Here, have another escargot."

Getting up to speed on the source code was the place where the language barrier with Sebastián was slowing them down the most.

The iOS app was one example. Jason's team already had a lot of that code completed to begin with, and the Colombians should have been able to reuse and build upon it. However, because Sebastián's English wasn't the best, it was taking him a little longer than expected to read the code and comments, and then ask the questions he needed to ask of the ShapeShift team to move forward efficiently.

But the most irritating problem—mainly because Jason didn't see why it had to be a problem at all—was Marion's inability to cooperate with Almendra.

"I can't work with this woman," she'd declared one day, tight-lipped, when Jason stopped by to ask how it was going. "She just *does things* and doesn't tell me."

"Like what?" Jason asked, already regretting his decision to drop in on her. It had been a long morning as it was.

"Like she just added in a feature to retrieve information from the nutrition database in either English or metric units—*in the middle of a sprint!*" Marion ranted.

"Did it work?" said Jason.

"That's not the point." Marion lifted her nose and twisted her engagement ring. "She has to *tell me* when she does these things. We have a process in place *for a reason*. What if it hadn't worked? How would I have known?"

Oh, I bet we would have noticed somehow, Jason thought. Out loud, he changed the subject. "I know you'll find a way to make it work with her. Hey," he nodded at the ring. "How's the venue search going?"

Marion glanced down at the ring, then back up at him. "We booked a place," she said shortly.

"That's great! I told you it would work out," Jason smiled, trying to seize on something positive. "Where is it going to be?"

"At the Computer History Museum," said Marion, flat and expressionless. Then she'd turned her back on him to continue wrestling with whatever problem she'd been working on before he'd interrupted.

Long story short: Jason had spent the better part of three months putting out one small fire after the next. Although, as silver linings went, he had to admit that he was a half-decent firefighter.

The time difference was the easiest fix. He'd rescheduled the onsite team's daily recaps to happen two hours earlier, before the end of the Colombian workday, so that the offshore team could participate. Mornings were trickier, but a little digging revealed that one of Ravi's developers—Shawn—woke up at the crack of dawn every morning for a two-hour workout before coming into the office, anyway. He had no problem swapping around his routine and being available for the Colombians at seven in the morning, then heading out to exercise after the rest of the Shape-

Shift team showed up for the day. Marion also agreed—somewhat grudgingly—to start earlier, provided that she could work remotely between 7:00 a.m. and 9:00 a.m.

With that system in place, progress moved a little quicker.

They also picked up speed thanks to—of all things—one of Ravi's jokes.

"My mother always told me I'd regret not paying more attention in Spanish class," he sighed one day after yet another miscommunication with Sebastián over the source code.

Jason was bent over a computer screen with him when Ravi said it, trying to help him untangle the mess. He frowned, the pen in his hand tapping a light rhythm on the desk beside the laptop. Without meaning to, Ravi had a point: a Spanish speaker on the ShapeShift team would probably eliminate 80 percent of the errors they'd been fixing. But they didn't have anyone bilingual in Spanish. Most developers were more interested in learning new programming languages than human ones.

Then he remembered.

"*Yes*," he said loudly, banging the pen against the table with a triumphant *crack*.

Ravi stared at him—caught too off guard even to make fun of Jason's outburst.

"I'll be back," Jason said, and without a backward glance, he dropped Ravi and headed to his office to look up the résumé he needed.

Four days later, Pete—of Latin American Peace Corps fame—was on the payroll.

"You're here to rescue us, I hear," Ravi greeted him when Jason introduced them for the first time.

Pete chuckled as he shook his hand. *"Si señor,"* he replied. *"Soy la brigada de rescate."*

"I didn't catch that," Ravi cocked his head.

"I'm here to save you gringos," Pete smiled.

And he did. Not only did he bridge the communication gap with Sebastián, he brought along a healthy dose of invaluable cultural knowledge as well.

One Monday about a week after Pete joined the team, Jason walked into the office to find Marion in a mild state of panic. "I can't get a hold of the Colombians," she said. "None of them. Not a single person is answering my messages, Jason. I've been trying to get through for *two hours.*" Behind her, even Ravi looked serious.

Pete, walking in shortly after Jason, overheard the end of her speech.

"Hey, it's Colombian Mother's Day," he said. "They have it off. Chill pill, guys."

Between the more flexible schedule and Pete's mediation, the state of the union began to improve. Still, it felt like every time Jason plugged one hole in the bottom of their boat, another leak sprang up. Patrick had warned him from the start that there would be an acclimation period in working with the outsource team.

I'm not sure how much more acclimation I can take, he thought.

* * *

"Which do you like better: the elegant white one or this orange one with the black stippling on its tail?"

It was Jason's first day off from the relentless ShapeShift circus in three weeks, and Paula had dragged him out of bed at eight o'clock in the morning to go—of all things—fish shopping.

Despite ongoing difficulties with the landscapers, the koi pond was almost finished. Unfortunately, it was the only thing that was almost finished. Everything else was in varying states of half-started, started wrong, or not started at all. Jason thought of Mike's original promise to have the entire backyard done in three months and snorted under his breath. At this rate, it would take twice that long.

"Jay? *Jason.*" Paula's voice snapped him out of it.

"Yeah, here. What?" Jason answered, rubbing one bleary eye with the heel of his hand.

"I said, 'Which koi do you like better?'" Paula repeated, a thread of annoyance in the words.

"What's the difference?" Jason retorted. He tried for a sigh of exasperation. It came out as a yawn of exhaustion instead. "They're *fish.*"

"They're not just *fish,*" Paula rejoined, giving him a look. "They're living art. Expensive and *long*-living art, Jason. A hundred dollars a koi, and we're stuck with them for thirty years. You expect me to choose them blindfolded?"

Jason was about to retort that he expected her to choose them any way she wanted, as long as he didn't have to be involved, when his phone buzzed. He pulled it out of his pocket and found a text message from Ravi.

> You asked me to let you know the peak load test results . . . not good? 😣 Slow performance and multiple timeouts. We need an architecture tune-up.

He sighed and ran a hand through his hair, texting back his location and saying he'd be there soon. At least it would save him from the impending marital squabble.

"I have to go," he told Paula. "They need me at the office. It's urgent."

She huffed. "What about the koi?"

"You choose," Jason said, barely holding back an eye roll as he headed for the door. "Just promise you won't name them!" he called over his shoulder before he escaped.

They had ridden their bikes into town, and the ShapeShift office was less than ten minutes away. Jason rode over there, struggling to stay alert enough to keep himself from getting run over by a bus. Or an umbrella motorbike.

When he walked into the office, he found Ravi—and Pete.

"Jason, I was just about to text you," Ravi said, looking a little sheepish—but only a little. "We figured it out."

"Pete?" Jason asked, squinting to make sure he was awake. "Aren't you off today?"

"I was around the corner at In-N-Out," Pete said with an easy smile, shaking a slightly greasy white paper bag. "When Ravi texted me, I figured I'd might as well just stop in."

"I'm not used to having him around yet," Ravi added, "or I would've contacted him first. Sorry."

"No, no, that's . . . fine," Jason yawned. "I'm glad you guys sorted it out."

"Yeah, we're good," Ravi assured him. Then he added with a grin, "Are you going to rejoin your wife on the fish search?"

"And waste this golden opportunity?" Jason said, turning to go. "If I play my cards right, I can get three more hours of sleep while she debates the aesthetic appeal of every scale on their bodies. I'm going home."

THIRTEEN

The "Little" Stuff

By the end of the third month, quick check-ins by phone weren't cutting it anymore. Jason asked Patrick if they could sit down in person and discuss some serious strategies for working with the outsourcing team.

Which was how he ended up at Menara Moroccan Restaurant.

What does this guy have against normal food? Jason sighed, pushing through the front door into a wide room splashed in blues, golds, and reds. Low tables were scattered everywhere, surrounded by squat floor cushions. Middle Eastern tilework ran halfway up the walls, and elaborate metal lamps and Arabic motifs decorated the long wooden beams in the ceiling. The smell of spices singed Jason's nostrils.

He spotted Patrick at one of the tables in the center of the room and made his way over to join him.

"You look like hell," Patrick said by way of a greeting when Jason sat down, his gray eyes taking in the stress and fatigue that were part and parcel of Jason's face these days. "Want me to teach you some Indian pranayamas?"

Jason thought back to Patrick's show of bizarre breathing exercises at the Turkish restaurant. "I'll pass," he said. "Thanks anyway."

"Suit yourself," Patrick shrugged. "All right, lay it on me. What ails you, young Jason?"

"What doesn't?" Jason groaned. He took a breath, trying to decide where to begin. "Well—"

He was about to launch into an explanation of how miscommunication over the BurnRate application architecture was still causing delays when the lights dimmed, a drumbeat struck up, and a belly dancer decked out in blue sequins sashayed onto the red carpet of the dining area. The patrons at the other tables whooped and applauded her arrival. A high-pitched string instrument pierced the air from hidden loudspeakers.

Jason had to be back at ShapeShift in less than an hour. Irritated, he leaned over the table to try to talk to Patrick above the music—only to be blocked by Patrick's hand signaling him into silence.

Apparently, enjoying the performance took precedence over saving Jason's hide.

Jason sat back on his cushion, resisting the impulse to start tapping his pen on the table. Instead, he set his jaw, crossed his arms over his chest, and waited for the dance to end.

It took a full five minutes.

When it was finally over, Patrick applauded the dancer off the floor along with the rest of the restaurant. Then he saw Jason's face, grinned, and slapped him on the back. "Chief, you gotta lighten up," he said. "Life isn't that serious."

That did it.

"Really?" Jason fumed. "I have three months left to build the most complex nutrition software I've ever seen, and we're not even halfway there. My product owner refuses to cooperate with my scrum master. I can't go near her without being dragged into some one-sided drama or getting bombarded with complaints. We're *still* running into issues helping the Colombians get clarity on the architecture—even with Pete around to translate. I've got an impatient CEO breathing down my neck because a board of impatient VCs are breathing down his.

"You think my life isn't that serious?" he went on, relentless. "Tell me, Patrick, have you ever been the reason an entire company crumbles and more than a dozen people lose their jobs?"

"Worse," Patrick said lightly, not even batting an eye. "I'll have the potato tagine with red chermoula," he told the waiter, whom Jason hadn't even seen appear at his elbow.

The waiter nodded and scribbled down the order, then looked at Jason. Jason blinked.

"Um—I'll take a kebab," he said, citing the only Moroccan food he knew.

"Lamb, chicken, prawn, or vegetable?" the server asked.

"Yes. Er, I mean lamb," Jason managed.

The server thanked them and left to put in the order.

"Look," Patrick said as the man walked away, "you're getting hung up on the little stuff."

Jason bristled. "*Little* stuff?"

"How's the quality of the work?" Patrick demanded evenly.

Jason glared at him for a moment, defiant. But there was only one honest answer to the question. "It's excellent," he admitted, feeling a tiny bit of tension leave his shoulders. "When it gets done, it looks amazing. But the hang-ups along the way are killing us."

Patrick nodded. "What that means is that you've got a baby somewhere in all that bathwater—one worth keeping." He poured himself a cup of mint tea from a metal teapot that the waiter must have left on their table. "If your problem isn't the work itself, then it has to do with the people doing the work. What are the fifth and sixth keys of software outsourcing?"

Jason looked at him. Patrick looked back, never breaking eye contact as he took a sip of the tea. It took Jason a moment to realize that Patrick actually expected him to answer the question.

"You know, it's funny," he said humorlessly, "but even with all the spare time I've had lately, I've somehow still failed to memorize your handouts."

Patrick laughed his usual roar of a laugh, and several heads turned their way. Jason shrank on his cushion.

"Fifth key of software outsourcing," Patrick quoted with a grin. "'Think like a partner and embrace cultural differences.' And trust me, chief, you've got it easy on this one."

"Really," Jason said flatly.

"Really," Patrick nodded, lifting his teacup in a toast. "The learning curve could be worse. You think you've got communication issues? In Asia, it's impolite to say no to anything."

Jason narrowed his eyes, interested in spite of himself. "How does that work?"

"There's a code," Patrick explained. "I wrote a blog post about it: The Seven Ways an Indian Programmer Says 'No.' You just learn to recognize the subtle 'no's, and you're good to go. Then at the opposite end of the spectrum you've got your Eastern Europeans, who are so straightforward that they can actually come off as offensive sometimes—even though the points they're making are usually right."

Jason frowned. "What do they do about it? The people who hire them?" he asked.

"They do the same thing you're going to do," Patrick said. "Learn how to communicate. As long as you agree on your fundamental values—and you do—then you can deal with the rest.

Don't let people take things personally. It's your product owner who's got her feathers all ruffled up, you said?"

"Right. Marion." Jason passed the palm of his hand over his forehead. It gave him a headache just thinking about it. "She's convinced that Almen—that our scrum master disrespects her, because the scrum master doesn't check in with Marion about every little thing she does. That, and the scrum master likes to laugh."

"The scrum master laughs *at* her?" Patrick asked, raising an eyebrow.

"No," Jason said. "Just in general. They're Colombians; they enjoy enjoying themselves—at least the ones I met. But Marion insists that she's being mocked."

"Sounds like you and Marion could both learn to laugh a little more," Patrick grinned, and Jason scowled at him. "See? Case in point," the older man added, acknowledging the scowl. "Your product owner needs to stop making everything into a personal battle. She's treating the differences between her and the scrum master like a barrier. You've got to get her to embrace them instead. Find things that she and the scrum master have in common and can get excited about together."

"I'm all for it. What do you propose? Hypnosis?" Jason suggested, unable to keep the sarcasm at bay.

"Good guess, but no," Patrick countered. "I propose the sixth key of software outsourcing: 'The relationship is as important as technical requirements and capabilities.'"

Jason felt the fight go out of him. In its place, there was just exhaustion. "Look, Patrick, I agree with you. I do. I really want everyone to get along. But we have *three months* to finish this thing." He sighed. "I just don't have time to send everyone to an inner child workshop."

"You don't have time *not* to," Patrick said, though, for once, Jason almost imagined that he caught a ray of sympathy in the gray eyes. "A strong relationship between your teams is what will pull everyone together to make your deadline. Without it, you don't stand a chance."

"Why?" Jason blurted, exasperated. "Why can't everyone just act like adults and do their jobs? Why do I have to jump through hoops just to get a little clarity and cooperation out of them?"

Patrick sat back on his cushion and rubbed his chin with one hand, his eyes never leaving Jason—as if pondering the best way to break into Jason's head. "What happened when you broke bread with the teams you visited, abroad?" he asked.

Jason groaned quietly, already seeing where this was going. But he answered the question anyway. "They became real people," he admitted.

Patrick nodded. "And from 'real people,' you get everything else. Effective communication. A personal bond. Equal investment in the project from both parties. Efficiency. All of that happens because your offshore team isn't separate from your onsite team—it's an extension of it. It happens because your teams are friends, and they have each other's backs." He leaned back toward the table and poured himself more tea. "You know better than most that software development is an art. It's not something you can build with machines. It takes creative people to make it happen—and when you've got a lot of people working together, it also takes true partnership." He pushed the teapot away, folded his hands, and leveled a look at Jason. "BurnRate isn't the minor leagues. You're slaying Goliath with this thing. If you had more time and less to do, you could keep taking the scenic route—"

Scenic route? Jason thought. *Through where? A post-apocalyptic war zone?*

"—but you don't have time, and if you want to get the results you're talking about, you need to take the shortcut," Patrick went on. "You have to give your team members the same opportunity you had. You have to let them meet the people they're working with."

Jason stared at him, deadpan. "You want me to fly my Silicon Valley team down to Colombia?"

"The key players, yes," Patrick said. "Your product owner and your lead developer, at least. Probably also Pete the translator. Not just for the soft skills, either," he added after another sip of tea. "People challenges are best resolved face to face, true—but so is explaining the source code, user stories, architecture, or whatever. The trip may seem like a big stone, but you'll kill a lot of birds with it. Trust me."

"So let me get this straight," Jason mumbled, pressing his fingers to his temples to keep the overwhelm from setting in. "I fly my team down to Colombia once, and all my troubles will be over?"

"Well, the 'once' is relative," Patrick amended. "I recommend letting people connect in person every quarter. When you're working together on a large, long-term engagement, anyway."

"Every *quarter?*"

"*When* you're working together long term. Look, you just told me you want to get rid of the headaches and the hassles and the fighting and the stress," Patrick pointed out. "I'm telling you how to get rid of all that. You turn your team leaders into friends, and all the suspicion and accusations will stop. They'll get along. In fact, they'll *more* than get along; they'll actually enjoy working together. That's when you'll see the results you're after."

Jason gave up. He propped his elbows on the table, dropped his face into his hands, and groaned. "My CFO is going to kill me," he mumbled.

"Hey," Patrick said, and Jason looked up through his fingers. The corner of Patrick's mouth had twitched upward. "You're doing a great job," he said, with as much empathy as Jason had heard from him yet. "Some adjusting needs to happen when you first start working with an outsourced team—but the worst is almost over. Don't worry too much about your CFO. He'll see for himself that the investment in getting the teams to connect pays off in the business, in the end."

Then, like an elusive endangered species, the empathy vanished, replaced by Patrick's standard lighthearted grin. "Now stop hogging up the table space, chief," he said. "The food is here."

Jason glanced sideways and saw that the server had once again appeared at his shoulder, this time balancing their lunch. Reluctantly, he dragged his elbows off the table. Then he picked listlessly at his kebab, picturing how overjoyed Michael would be to hear about the group trip to Medellín, as Patrick tucked into his tagine with gusto.

"Cheer up, kid. It's not an execution," Patrick teased.

"Wanna bet?" Jason muttered. *This is going to be interesting . . .*

FOURTEEN

Breaking Bread

"I swear, if I trip over *one* more shovel lying in the driveway, some-one is going to get buried with it."

Jason was alone in the conference room at MedellínTech, listening to Paula rant about the latest in their unfolding backyard soap opera. Half his mind was elsewhere. The second afternoon of the ShapeShift team's two-day trip to Colombia was drawing to a close—and, all told, it had been a success.

Really, the biggest challenge had been getting here in the first place, Jason reflected. His showdown with Michael had been a battle for the ages, as expected. But in the end—again with a little help from Scott—the travel budget had been approved.

From there, life had gotten better.

He'd arrived in Colombia three days later with Ravi, Marion, and Pete in tow. As on his first visit, Ramón had kindly picked them up from the airport and driven them down into the valley. Ravi ate up the spectacular view, bombarding Ramón with questions and jokes, and Pete seemed right at home. Only Marion kept her silence, hands folded stiffly in her lap, lips pressed into a tight line.

"I don't have time to go on this trip," she'd argued with Jason when he'd told her what was happening. "I have deadlines to

meet—professional *and* personal. Weddings don't plan themselves," she'd added hotly.

He'd insisted that she come anyway, a move that had landed
him in the doghouse and left him with a product owner who was
not on good terms with her scrum master *or* her VP of engineering.

This had better work, Delaney, Jason had thought, following the
others into the four-story plaster-fronted building when they had
finally arrived at MedellínTech. Ramón had taken them to the
same conference room Jason had used on his first visit. This time,
it was empty. "I will let the others know you are here." Ramón had
given them a quick smile and left to make good on his promise.

In the two minutes of silence that followed, Jason had watched
Marion out of the corner of his eye. If possible, her face was grim-
mer than ever. She looked like a foot soldier on the front lines,
bracing herself for battle.

Then the Colombian team all but burst through the door.

Andrés, Marco, and Sebastián headed straight for Ravi and
Pete, the lot of them an indistinguishable mass of smiles and warm
welcomes. But Jason's eyes were on his product owner. As soon as
she saw Almendra, Marion set her jaw, lifted her chin, and roboti-
cally extended her hand. *Here we go,* Jason thought with a sinking
stomach.

Fortunately, Almendra turned out to be as oblivious to other
people's judgment as Patrick.

With a warm, belly-deep laugh, the scrum master grabbed
Marion's stiff hand and unceremoniously yanked her into a hug.
Jason barely bit back a chuckle himself as Marion's eyes popped
open in shock.

"At last you are here!" Almendra declared, pulling back from
the hug without releasing her grip on Marion's shoulders. She
smiled ear to ear, as if gazing upon her long-lost sister. Then she
hugged her one more time for good measure, linked her elbow with

Marion's, and started in the direction of the door, saying, "Come, I will show you everything."

The entire trip was worth it, Jason thought, just for the look of utter discombobulation on Marion's face as she was led away.

It was a foregone conclusion that the others would get along—and they did. Pete was an instant hit by sheer virtue of his ability to speak Spanish. Ravi and Marco instantly became a human feedback loop of jokes. Even Sebastián opened up more than Jason had ever seen, put at ease by the security blanket of "translator Pete," as Patrick called him. A few minutes after Almendra and Marion had disappeared, the men had followed suit, heading off to put everyone on the same page about the architecture of the BurnRate app once and for all.

Jason's main purpose in coming along had been for continuity. Over the course of the next two days, he checked in on everyone from time to time—but mainly he stayed stationed in the conference room with his laptop, drinking mediocre coffee and doing the same work he would have been doing at home. Now and then, a distant "Marco!" "Polo!" sounded from somewhere in the office beyond.

". . . and now, they've actually lost the master list of materials," Paula was saying.

That got Jason's full attention. "What?" he said.

"They've lost it. It's gone," Paula repeated, her words laced with frustration.

"When?" Jason asked.

"I don't know. Probably a while ago," said Paula with a little snort of disgust. "I found out because I noticed they were installing the wrong flagstones. They're supposed to be 'Cherry Blend,' and instead they got 'Chiaroscuro.' Apparently the name sounded right to the worker who picked them up—and he didn't have the list to check the spelling. Now they have to redo the whole thing." He could almost hear her rolling her eyes over the phone. "One more thing lost in translation."

Jason ran a hand through his hair. "Did you talk to Manuel?" he asked.

"That's the worst part," Paula said grimly. "He's gone."

"Please be kidding," Jason said.

"I'm not kidding," Paula told him.

Jason expelled a breath, pulled out his pen, and started tapping it on the tabletop. "He just left without saying anything, like all the others?" After José had vanished without a trace that first week, they'd lost three more landscapers over the course of the next three months. All of them had ditched the project like José: without a word.

"No," Paula sighed. "He told me he was going, at least. Said that he was very sorry, but he couldn't work with Mike anymore, and he'd found another job elsewhere."

With his free hand, Jason pinched the bridge of his nose. "There goes our last hope," he muttered.

"I can't believe they lost the *master list*," Paula said, picking up the rant where she'd left off, before Jason asked about Manuel. "And I can't believe myself for writing it out by hand. Who does that anymore, Jason? Who even *uses* pens?"

Jason glanced at the tapping pen in his hand and quietly returned it to his pocket. "No one," he mumbled. But he knew the loss of the list wasn't Paula's fault. Not really. "I'm sorry I handed the list over to them in the first place," he apologized. "I wasn't thinking."

There was a pause at the other end of the line, as though Paula were debating whether to lay into him about it. Then she sighed. "As long as you don't drag me back to New Jersey, I'll forgive you anything," she said. "How's the powwow going down there?"

"Really well, actually," Jason told her, glad to change the subject. "The Colombian team is all clear on the software architecture now, we think. And it looks like Marion and Almendra have actually become friends."

"Wow. Does this mean you get a Nobel Prize for ending World War III?" Paula asked, adding under her breath, "And if it does, can we use the prize money to pay for better landscapers?"

"I didn't do anything," Jason smiled. "The two of them took off together as soon as we got here. Every time I catch a glimpse of them, they're thick as thieves, going over systems and processes— or whatever they're doing. They didn't even join us for dinner last night because Almendra wanted to introduce Marion to someone . . . Almendra's sister, I think."

A sudden "Marco!" "Polo!" sounded beyond the conference room door, followed by a collective hoot of laughter. The voices were headed Jason's way.

"Honey, listen, I have to go. I'll call you back when we get to the airport," he said.

Jason had barely hung up the phone when Marion and Almendra walked into the room, Ravi, Marco, and Pete close on their heels. Ravi and Marco were still snickering in the aftermath of their bottomlessly entertaining Marco Polo joke. Almendra had her hand on Marion's shoulder, and both of them looked happy as clams.

Jason raised an eyebrow. "All good?" he asked.

Marion grinned at Almendra, then gave him a nod. "Yep," she said. "Good."

FIFTEEN

Jumping Ship

t turned out that Almendra's sister was a wedding planner.

Jason had heard more about it than he'd ever wanted to know on the plane ride back to California. In fact, he'd never heard Marion talk so much in his life. When the scrum master had found out that Marion was getting married, Almendra had told her one horror story after another about nearly botched weddings, and how her sister—superhero-like—had swooped in to save the day. Then the sister herself had told Marion even more stories on the night when they'd all had dinner together at Almendra's house.

"They *understand*," Marion had enthused on the flight, oblivious to the glazed-over stares of her all-male audience, her eyes shining as if she'd discovered the Holy Grail itself.

She had devoured the sympathy and advice the way a desert wanderer chugs down water, Jason thought. That, combined with seeing for herself how well things were organized on Almendra's end—and how much Almendra laughed *in general* as opposed to *at* anyone—seemed to have put Marion at ease. In the four weeks since they'd been back, she'd loosened her micromanaging grip over the scrum master considerably, and things had been going smoothly between them ever since.

In fact, things had been going smoothly in general, Jason thought, cautiously allowing the concept into his mind as he left his office, heading over to ShapeShift's conference room for another meeting with the executive team. He was still working around the clock. However, now there was one key difference in the system:

The machinery was fully functional.

Marion and Almendra weren't the only success story from the trip to Colombia. Issues with the product architecture almost never came up anymore. Sebastián really was a genius, and he'd caught on quickly once he had a clear and comprehensive explanation of how it worked. They'd hit the goals of the last sprint with flying colors, and the next one was off to a very promising start.

Before, the long hours were devoted to fixing problems. Now, they were resulting in real progress. *Maybe we will actually pull this monster off,* Jason had caught himself thinking just that morning.

In fact, ShapeShift wasn't even his biggest source of stress anymore; his backyard was. Yesterday, he'd watched Mike silently and grudgingly hand out paychecks to a line of equally silent and resentful workers. *No wonder they fly the coop in the middle of the night,* Jason thought. *No wonder none of them care about getting the job done right.*

Still, he reflected, arriving at the conference room and letting himself in through the glass door, all things considered, he was more grateful for the recent success with BurnRate than he was frustrated with the backyard. *At least I have a backyard to landscape, if we save ShapeShift,* he thought, nodding a hello at Lisbeth as he took his usual seat next to her at the table. Scott and Michael were already there.

Lance was the last to arrive.

Scott greeted them as the CTO sat down, and Jason waited for the green light to give his usual report on progress. He was even looking forward to it for once, he realized.

Instead, Scott looked at Lance. "Lance has some news," he said, stone faced.

Lance looked at the group and, as easily as if he were sharing the weather, said, "I've handed in my resignation. I'll be leaving ShapeShift next week."

A dead silence fell. Lisbeth and Michael stared at Lance. The look on his face was so casual and unrepentant that, for a moment, Jason honestly thought he was joking.

But he didn't take it back, didn't crack a smile and tell them it was all a bad joke.

The bastard was serious.

Jason found his voice. "Have you lost your mind?" he demanded.

Lance shrugged him off. "I've already contributed everything you need from me. You'll be fine."

"You *have* lost your mind," Jason insisted. His stomach had dropped through the floor, and he could feel the blood pounding in his temples. "How can you possibly pull this now? *Now?* We're *two months* away from the launch."

Jason's anger was contagious. Lance took the bait.

"How can I pull this now?" he retorted. "Gee, I don't know. Maybe because our VCs have fed us to the sharks? Maybe because we're outsourcing software development to the murder capital of the world? This entire circus was doomed to crash and burn from the beginning," he said. "I'm not sticking around for that joyride."

"*Traidor,*" Lisbeth muttered in Portuguese. Michael's face looked more like a bulldog's than Jason had ever seen it. The CFO was red, too furious to speak.

Jason fought to get his own fury back under control. "Lance, I've been trying to include you on the progress with the offshore team from the beginning," he started. "We ran into some delays at first, but the operation is up and running now. We're nailing our sprints. There's an honest-to-god chance that we'll actually make this happen—but not without you." He took a deep breath and tried to sound reasonable. "Please don't drop the ball on us. Not now."

"There's no ball to drop. I told you, you have everything you need," Lance replied, unmoved. "I've already accepted a position at another company. It's done."

This time, the silence stretched on longer than before. Jason had nothing left to say. He'd spent the last four months constructing an emergency pillar underneath the company to keep it from crumbling. Now Lance had knocked out one of ShapeShift's stable legs in one fell swoop. And there was no way to rebuild it. Not in time.

He felt as sick as he had at the "emergency mystery meeting" four months ago, when the VCs had dropped the bomb of software outsourcing on them in the first place.

Scott finally broke the tension in the room. "Lance needs to do what he needs to do," he said, his voice all formality. "I'll start looking for his replacement." Then he turned to Jason. In his eyes, Jason saw doom speeding his way even before he heard the official words.

"Jaye, until we find a new CTO, all of Lance's developers will report to you."

SIXTEEN

Isn't It . . . Complicated?

J ason sat at his desk, in his quiet office, alone for what seemed like the first time in days. The peaceful bubble of space around him felt like a crazy paradox.

In the space of a week, his life had spiraled into utter chaos.

Lance's declaration that he'd left Jason with everything Shape-Shift needed had turned out to be laughable, to say the least. The CTO had departed for good two days before he was supposed to present his conclusions to the company about the architectural approach of what still needed to be done on BurnRate. In his place, Jason was left with a vague, confusing write-up and a handful of even more confusing slides—along with a group of developers who expected him to have answers to things he just didn't have the answers to.

The answers were out of reach, in Lance's brain.

Lance had had expertise in areas that Jason knew almost nothing about. The man understood the complexity of the algorithm they needed to implement for BurnRate's food analysis feature. He had deep knowledge of image processing—also crucial to Burn-Rate's success. He understood the specs of what needed to be done. His developers were working with a NoSQL database they'd never used before, and they needed guidance during the implementation process—guidance that Lance was qualified to give, and Jason wasn't.

"How does this work?" they asked Jason, knocking on his office door one after the next. "Which database do we use to store the image data?"

Jason didn't know.

He also figured out pretty quickly that the MongoDB versus Cassandra internal benchmark debate that Lance had promised to take care of had never been resolved. On Thursday, he'd wasted an entire hour listening to Lance's team argue about it back and forth before Jason himself had finally stepped in. "All right, enough. Which one will get the job done more quickly with less risk?" he demanded.

With a few grumbles from the dissenters, the team finally settled on MongoDB.

But the questions about the image processing algorithm were what really killed him. Lance had planned to introduce a machine-learning approach that would improve the image-processing and recognition features of BurnRate over time. Unfortunately for everyone, Jason wasn't familiar with machine learning, either.

Before Lance had jumped ship, Jason had been keeping his head above water. It hadn't been easy. Even with the outsourcing situation under control, he had been maxed out, but he'd managed to keep all the balls in the air nonetheless—which he considered a success. Now he was flying blind, struggling to fix problems that he wasn't qualified to fix. Worse, the VCs were no happier about Lance's sudden departure than anyone else. They were heaping pressure on Scott to show them that Lance's team was still on track despite the loss of their captain—pressure that was ending up in Jason's lap. And to top it all off, Scott's emergency search for a new CTO was coming up empty. There was no sign of a replacement for Lance in sight.

Jason caught himself staring into the middle distance like a war refugee. He inhaled a long, slow breath and tried to pull it together. Not everything had fallen hopelessly to pieces, he reminded himself. In the midst of total pandemonium, the outsource team, at least, seemed to be rolling dependably along.

As if on cue, Marion tapped on the doorframe and strolled into Jason's office . . . humming.

Marion never hummed.

"Good morning!" she said brightly, and launched into a report on the latest sprint. Jason barely heard what she was saying. He was too busy wondering which alien species had seized control of her mind. *No one should be able to exude so much happiness and calm at a time like this—least of all Marion.*

"You're cheerful today," he commented when she was done with her report.

A smile broke across her face. "I found a venue!" she gushed, beaming. "I don't have to have my wedding at the Computer History Museum after all. I'm getting married in Colombia!"

Jason listened in baffled silence as Marion explained her plans. The place they'd found was beautiful. The timing couldn't be more perfect—and neither could the price.

"Isn't it . . . complicated?" Jason managed, finally finding his voice.

Marion waved a dismissive hand. "No, no. Almendra and her sister are handling everything. It's going to be perfect." Her phone buzzed, and she turned to go. "You're invited, of course!" she threw over her shoulder before flitting out the door.

Right, Jason thought, watching her float away, *assuming I'm still alive by then. If this job doesn't kill me, New Jersey will.*

His own phone rang, and he picked it up.

"Hello?"

"Jason? It's me," said Paula's voice. He couldn't tell if she sounded more flustered or frustrated. "I can't make it home to meet the landscapers again. I have another emergency at the clinic."

Jason ran a stressed hand through his hair. "What's going on?" he asked.

"Rocket fuel," Paula said.

"Really? Them again?"

"No, different kids," Paula told him. "Girls, actually."

"Girls?" Jason repeated, confused. Then, "How many rocket fuel start-ups are there?" he muttered.

"Two, apparently," Paula's sigh sounded about as exasperated as he felt. "The leader of this one was booted from the team I patched up a couple months ago. She decided that they kicked her out for sexist reasons, and she put together an all-female team in response. They're determined to figure out the formula before the guys do. So basically," she concluded, "they've blown themselves up in the name of revenge."

Jason sat back in his chair. "Listen, Paula, I really can't leave. They need me here."

"What am I supposed to do? Let the kids bleed to death?" Paula retorted.

Jason closed his eyes and counted to five. Then he let out a resigned breath. "Fine. You win," he relented. "What are they doing on the backyard today, anyway?"

"They're putting in the palm trees."

"Do they need us to be there for that?" Jason said, snatching at a wisp of hope.

"Are you really asking me this question?" Paula deadpanned at the other end of the line.

She had a point.

"All right, all right," he sighed, collecting his things. "I'll go home."

"Thanks, honey. I'll see you tonight," Paula said, and hung up to go tend to her latest batch of mad scientists.

Jason sent a quick text to all his technical leads telling them what was going on and instructing them to call him if they needed him. Then, grumbling, he headed out the door.

* .... *

He pulled up to his house ten minutes later to find a crane looming over it, lowering the first of two squat, fat palm trees into the backyard from the back of a huge flatbed truck. As it inched along, the crane emitted a piercing *beep, beep, beep* noise. The neighbors were out in force for the show. *Of course*, Jason cringed.

He parked as discreetly as he could and went around back to check on progress.

A man he didn't recognize was standing in the yard with coils of metal cables hanging from his left shoulder, directing the crane.

Must be another newbie, Jason thought without surprise, walking up to him. He'd lost track of how many rounds of musical chairs Mike's team had been through over the past few months. "Hi," he shouted over the beeping crane when they were close enough to talk, extending his hand. "I'm Jason, the homeowner."

"Carlos," the man shouted back. He shook Jason's hand briefly before returning his gaze to the crane.

"Where's Mike?" Jason asked. Mike didn't often put in a personal appearance on the job site, but even he ought to be present for something this huge, Jason thought.

"Mike no here," Carlos shrugged, keeping his eyes on the crane.

Clearly, Jason managed not to say aloud. The landscapers were now a full forty days over their promised three-month completion date. Worse, they were barely more than halfway done with the backyard, thanks to ongoing mistakes and miscommunications.

He and Carlos stood silently together for a minute, watching the crane lower the first palm tree into a pit in the ground. Then Jason cleared his throat and leaned over to shout into Carlos's ear. "The trees just stay in the ground like that?" he asked.

"No, señor," Carlos replied, patting the thick steel cables on his shoulder. "We bolt them down."

Jason nodded, remembering. At some point, months ago, he and Paula had had to choose between an underground anchoring system or an over-ground one. They'd gone with the underground option—which was no doubt why Carlos's cables had strange, square metal feet attached to the ends.

"So . . ." Jason asked Carlos as casually as he could, "How did you find this job with Mike?" The question had been on his mind more and more lately, as worker after worker passed through the revolving door of his backyard.

Carlos glanced at him. "Home Depot," he said. Then he added something that sounded like, "Man, these things are heavy," and shifted the cables off his shoulder.

Well. That explains a lot, Jason thought, helping Carlos lower the cables to the ground. Which was when he noticed that they were standing on the wrong flagstones. Again. They had actually gotten the order wrong a second time.

Paula was going to kill someone.

He took a deep breath and waited for the incessant beeping to stop so he could talk to Carlos at a normal decibel level. This conversation might take a while . . .

When Paula trudged through the front door late that night, she looked as exhausted as Jason felt. They didn't talk. They didn't read the news. They just ate cereal for dinner and stumbled upstairs to bed.

"The landscapers put in the wrong flagstones again," Jason told her as they lay on their backs, staring like zombies at the ceiling.

Paula made a sound like "hngh" by way of acknowledgment, as if she lacked the energy even to be indignant.

"I told them the right name and . . . wrote it down," Jason yawned. "The palm trees look all right, at least. Thank god we bought landscaping insurance before this started."

Paula didn't respond for so long that he thought she'd fallen asleep. Then, "Mhm," she mumbled, only half coherent as she drifted off. "Otherwise . . . there'd be a few more patients in my clinic. I'd put them there myself . . . with that damned shovel I keep tripping over, in the driveway . . . just to make sure they get . . . the point."

SEVENTEEN

A Pile of Flashlights

A couple days later, Jason met Patrick at the One World office. The appointment was just a standard check-in, scheduled weeks ago. He didn't need it. The outsourcing team was fine; it was the rest of life that had turned berserker on him. By all rights, Jason should have canceled the meeting and put the extra hour to better use at ShapeShift, struggling to keep their doomed ship from sinking.

But he didn't cancel the meeting. Mainly, if he were being honest with himself, because he could really use a reminder right now that "life isn't that serious."

Jason parked his Prius in front of the old train station and headed in. The place was starting to take shape, he noticed. A proper plaque had replaced the taped-up sign announcing One World headquarters, and most of the grime had been scrubbed from the glass doors and windows. Inside, on the first floor, some thin gray carpet and real chairs had replaced the rows of bolted-down wooden railway seating. A couple of exotic pictures hung on the walls, and Jason even noticed a reception desk—albeit unmanned.

Not bad, Delaney, he thought as he headed up the stairwell to Patrick's office.

Another client passed him en route, nodding at Jason as he took his leave. Jason almost stopped in his tracks and stared at the guy's retreating back in surprise. But, in the end, he pulled himself together and kept climbing.

Patrick was sprawled in the brown leather chair behind his elephant desk when Jason appeared in the doorway. The older man took one look at him and said, "That does it. I'm teaching you some Indian pranayamas whether you like it or not."

Jason waved him off and let himself into the still wild but better organized office, no longer thrown off by Ziggy the zebra rug or anything else. He half collapsed into one of the elephant chairs without a word, mostly because he had no idea where to start.

"You'd better start from the beginning," Patrick read his mind.

So Jason did.

"The outsourcing team is fine," he began. "But . . ." He told Patrick about Lance jumping ship. He told him about the tornado the CTO had left in his wake—a high-speed funnel of confusion, instability, and fire-breathing VCs.

"I can't handle this," Jason admitted, and somehow it was a relief to say it out loud. He felt like a foot soldier on the losing side at the tail end of the war: tired to the bone of fighting and ready for the battle to end, come what may. It wouldn't be long now. "I don't have the knowledge to lead Lance's team. We've tried to find a new CTO. No one can take over. Maybe if I had more time, I could build a solution . . . but I don't." Somewhere during the course of the explanation, he'd leaned his elbows forward onto his knees. His pen had found its way out of his pocket and into his hand, but he wasn't tapping it; instead, he was gripping it for dear life. "BurnRate is going to flop," he said flatly. "After all this. It's actually going to go down in flames."

Patrick had listened to the whole story without saying a word, his sharp gray eyes never leaving Jason. Now, finally, he spoke. "Kid, can I ask you something?" he said. "Do you torture yourself on purpose?"

Jason stared at him.

Patrick leaned back in his leather chair and linked his hands behind his head, the way he'd done the first day Jason met him. "Really, I'm curious," he went on. "Here you are, moaning about how dark it is while you sit on a mountain of flashlights. I know you're a bit of a pessimist, but come on," he cocked his head to the side. "This is taking it a little too far, don't you think?"

"Patrick," Jason said, too drained to be annoyed, "I haven't had a full night's sleep in about four months. Please. Have a little mercy and just tell me what the hell you're talking about."

Patrick sighed and pushed a sheet of paper across the desk at him—one that must have been left over from his last meeting. Jason glanced at it and saw that it was the same list Patrick had given him his first day.

"Seventh key of software outsourcing, chief," Patrick said. "Read it and stop weeping."

Jason read it:

Everything you invest in hiring a good outsourcing team will return to you threefold.

"If you think I have anything left to invest," Jason told him, "you're even crazier than I thought you were."

"I'll take that as a compliment," Patrick said with a half-smile. "But alas, I'm not that crazy. There's nothing left for you to invest in the seventh key of outsourcing, Jason—because you've already invested it.

"'Invest' means investing time, money, and relationship building. You've been doing all those things from the beginning," Patrick continued. "If you're careless about selecting a good outsourcing partner in the first place, you'll pay for it later. But you weren't careless. You put a lot of effort into choosing an innovative, passionate, competent team. Now, you get to reap the rewards of that."

"Yeah. Still not following," Jason said. "No sleep. Deprived brain neurons. Mercy, Patrick, remember?"

"MedellínTech can give you the stand-in CTO you need, genius," Patrick finally spelled it out.

Jason looked at him. Patrick looked back.

When the significance of the statement finally sank in, it hit Jason like a truck.

"I can do that?" he blurted.

"Why do you think we put them through that whole diehard vetting process to make sure they could create innovative software?" Patrick snorted. "Of course you can do that."

Jason couldn't speak, still trying to process the possibility of this unlikely salvation. He barely managed to keep an ear focused on the conversation as Patrick kept talking.

"You've got twenty-five developers on deck, Jaye. MedellínTech has more than four hundred," Patrick pointed out. "One of those four hundred brains is capable of coming up with the solutions you need. You didn't choose an outstanding team just so that they'd be able to handle your basic necessities. You chose them so that they'd be able to support you in ways that went far beyond what you first thought you'd use them for." He chuckled. "You just didn't know it until now."

Slowly, Jason's reeling mind began to right itself. "Well . . ." he muttered under his breath, "if it stands a chance of saving me from New Jersey, I'll take it."

Patrick raised an eyebrow. "Come again?" he asked.

"Nothing." Jason pushed his elbows off his knees. Then he pushed himself out of the chair. For the first time in days, there was a light at the end of the tunnel worth moving toward. "I've got to get going. I need to call my head of business development before the Colombians go home for the day." He smiled for what felt like the first time in weeks. "Thanks," he said, extending his hand.

Patrick took it, then shook his head, a smile in his eyes. "May the force be with you, chief," he said.

Jason turned and strode toward the door.

"Heads up!"

He turned just in time to catch a soft white ball flying toward his stomach.

"In case you need to blow off some steam," Patrick grinned.

Jason laughed, saluted him, and walked out the door.

On his way out of the train station, he unrolled the gift. The soft white part was a cotton shirt with wooden cogs for buttons. It had the One World logo printed across the back—and no shirt pocket.

Time to give up the pen-tapping habit anyway, Jason thought. *Who even uses pens anymore?*

The round part, buried in the middle of the shirt, was an egg-shaped Chinese flute like the ones Patrick kept on his desk. When he saw the two yin and yang koi fish carved into it, he had to laugh. "I wonder if your designs will live up to Paula's strict aesthetic standards," he grinned.

A couple of people were wandering around outside when Jason walked out into the parking lot. But, for once, he didn't care. So they might look at him like he was nuts. So what? What was the worst that could happen?

He brought the flute to his mouth, and blew.

EIGHTEEN

The Seventh Key

Half an hour later, Jason was back in his office with Ramón on Skype.

Ramón listened to Jason's account of Lance's departure with his usual sharp intensity, not a word slipping through the cracks. Then he said, "Tell me what you need."

Jason told him.

"Lance's team needs guidance," he admitted. "There's a lot of confusion with the NoSQL database. The nutritional information was implemented a long time ago, but now we're putting in the identification that will translate photographs into food, and the developers are running into questions I can't answer. They're not familiar with microservices and machine learning, either.

"We need someone who can help at a strategic technical level," he summed up bluntly.

Ramón's face was turned down away from the camera, taking notes. Jason waited for MedellínTech's head of business development to deliver the verdict, and realized he was holding his breath.

Finally, Ramón looked up. "I understand," he said, and the clarity and confidence in his voice was music to Jason's ears. "We can help."

"How soon?" Jason asked.

"Right away," Ramón told him. "We have software architecture experts with NoSQL and microservices experience. I'll identify the one who's most qualified and put him in contact with you tomorrow morning."

"That's incredible. Thank you," Jason told him. Then he added, curious, "You look like you're used to this."

"This?" Ramón repeated.

"Fielding last-minute calls of panic from distraught VPs of engineering," Jason clarified.

Ramón smiled. "We work with a lot of big companies," he said, "but we also work with a lot of start-ups. Some of them don't have CTOs at all. They hire us to fill that role for them. We will have someone take over the reins for you, ASAP."

"I appreciate it," Jason thanked him again, and meant it. He wasn't sure he'd appreciated anything more in his life.

"You're very welcome," Ramón assured him.

After the call ended, Jason sat back in his chair. He picked up the Chinese flute on the corner of his desk and turned it in his hands. Then he sighed, tossed it in the air, and caught it again.

All right, he thought. *Let's see how this goes.*

It worked.

The next morning, Ramón introduced Jason to Felipe, his new lead architect and acting CTO. Felipe was a more talkative version of Sebastián. Not only did he have experience with image processing, but he was also well versed in microservices and was tracking trends in data analytics and the machine learning space.

Jason didn't waste time. He arranged a virtual meeting between Felipe and Lance's team that same afternoon. The five strung-out developers hung on the Colombian lead architect's every word, then pelted him with an hour's worth of questions—as if he were a mirage and this was their one chance to ask everything they could think of before he vanished into thin air.

Felipe answered every one of them without batting an eye.

"Thank god," one of them sighed after Felipe had gone. Then he stole a glance at Jason and added, "No offense."

Jason laughed and shook his head. "None taken. On the contrary, I agree," he said. "Thank god."

A couple days later, Felipe reported that he agreed with Lance's prognosis: the machine learning approach was their best bet . . . eventually. However, he also estimated they would need an additional three to four months to implement these features. There was a risk of their schedule slipping further because of a shortage of data scientists and engineers familiar with the latest machine learning advances. Still, the necessity of postponing these features was a welcome relief for Jason. It was finally clear that ShapeShift had simply been trying to cram too much into the initial release of the BurnRate product.

Felipe also concurred that the selection of MongoDB was a reasonable choice for the NoSQL database. Even better, he sent a complete explanation detailing his reasons for condoning it. As he read through it, Jason felt the far-flung puzzle pieces of Lance's abandoned PowerPoint slideshow come together in his mind. Everything made sense.

"Let's do it," he confirmed.

And just like that, in the space of seventy-two hours, Lance's team was moving full speed ahead again.

The CTO's developers wisely went straight to Felipe with their questions—which left Jason free to return to his own skyscraper of a workload. As the days ticked by, the hours that he and everyone else put into the project became longer. But now, at least, he wasn't at the helm of a sinking ship. Now, the machinery was up and running again, thanks to MedellínTech's impressive rescue operations.

Delaney was right, Jason mused when both teams hit every goal of their second-to-last sprint in spite of all odds. *I was sitting on a pile of flashlights all along.*

NINETEEN

Eureka!

"I've got it!" Jason announced to Paula one night, about two weeks before the BurnRate deadline was set to drop. "Our landscapers suck because they're terrible outsourcers!"

He had just gotten off the phone with Mike—again. This time, he and Paula had found a few coils of thick steel cables out in the corner of the yard, behind the palm trees . . . cables that looked a lot like the ones Carlos had said were meant to anchor the trees to the ground until the roots had time to settle in. The trees themselves seemed sturdy enough. But by now, they'd learned the hard way that you always had to triple check with these people.

Carlos himself had dropped off the team after the trees were installed, so Mike said he needed to check with the others. "I'll get back to you," he'd said, and he'd finally made good on his word four days later—at eight o'clock at night—and called to reassure them that the cables had been installed. "The ones you found must have been extras left on the job site," he said.

"It took him four days to figure that out. *Four days!*" Jason declared. He was loopy from lack of sleep, but the high from everything going well at work was getting him through it. Patrick was right, he decided. How serious was life, really, as long as you didn't have to move back to New Jersey? "It never would've taken him that long if Mike had outsourced the labor right. He's the worst outsourcer I've ever seen. And do you know why?"

"I can't imagine," Paula said flatly from her chair on the other side of the kitchen table. It had been another long day for her, too.

"Because," Jason explained cheerfully, clasping his hands behind his head and leaning his own kitchen chair back on two legs, "he chooses his team like he's scavenging at a thrift shop: he hires whoever he can find, as fast and cheap as he can find them. He doesn't vet them to make sure they have the right experience for the job first—so of course none of them know what they're doing. Do you know where he gets his workers? From the crowd of guys loitering around the Home Depot. Carlos told me so."

"Who's Carlos?"

"My point exactly," Jason nodded. "And Mike doesn't know who they are much better than we do. I'm sure of it. How often have we seen him, over the last six months? He never stops by. He never gives his people any guidance. He just tells them what to do and expects them to take care of it. No wonder they're incompetent and drop like flies. He treats them like dirt."

"Manuel knew what he was doing," Paula noted.

"True," Jason conceded, "but he was the exception to the rule. That's one good worker out of what? Sixteen? Twenty?"

"At least," Paula huffed.

"Precisely," Jason said. "Mike set himself up for disaster from the beginning. Heck, he's still going. The man is an ongoing horror movie. *Rick Looney II, The Return: Now with Garden Rakes,*" he concluded triumphantly, stretching in his chair.

"Jay?"

"Hm?"

"You realize that we ourselves are guilty of everything you just described," Paula pointed out dryly. "How did we find Mike, again? Through a friend of a friend at your work?"

Jason blinked at her for a moment. Then he busted up laughing.

"Not even!" he hooted, tears of hilarity or irony in his eyes—he couldn't tell which. "We found him through a friend of a backstabbing traitor—Lance! You're right. We *were* terrible outsourcers!"

"Honey," Paula said, arching one eyebrow at him, "you're scaring me."

Jason got a grip. It wasn't easy. "Hey," he managed when he was able to speak clearly again, "at least now we understand the torture chamber we've been living in."

"Yes, dear. You're a genius," Paula sighed. "Can your grand revelation actually fix our problem?"

Jason smiled at her. "Maybe I'll refer Mike to Patrick Delaney," he said.

TWENTY

The Stress Test

Jason was standing in the war room.

He'd been there for hours, along with everyone else on the ShapeShift development team, running the finished software through a slew of final tests. The war room's big screen was hooked up to Skype, and on it the Colombians were also assembled. Empty pizza boxes and takeout containers littered both sides of the screen.

Everyone had been pulling all-nighters for the last four days.

Jason shifted and re-crossed his arms over his chest. His shoulders were tense, and the vertebrae in his neck felt about as flexible as rocks. No one around him looked any better. Ravi was barely standing. Marion's face was pinched at the corners. Pete's huge hands were folded into a knot, propped up in front of him on the war room table, and he leaned on them so that the upper knuckles covered most of his mouth. Even the Colombians were as serious and intense as Jason had ever seen them: Almendra leaning forward with her brow furrowed, Marco right beside her; Felipe and Sebastián solemn faced, occasionally muttering to each other in Spanish under their breath; Andrés in the background, mirroring Jason's crossed-arms posture.

Everything had gone off without a hitch so far, thanks to MedellínTech's Agile test-driven development process. The software responded correctly to every input they threw at it across the spectrum of exercise, sleep, and nutrition. It worked fast, the design was clean and easy to use, and it ran smoothly on every major device they'd tried it on. They were on their last major test—a stress test designed to confirm that BurnRate would work with millions of devices and deliver results to thousands of users quickly and simultaneously—but no one had cracked a smile. The same test had failed a few days ago because of a missing "circuit breaker" piece of code needed to gracefully handle a timeout situation. Even though they thought they'd fixed the issue with software, it wasn't over until it was over. One bug could send them back to a drawing board they didn't have time to go back to.

Jason held his breath and waited for the stress test to finish.

On screen, shared with both teams over Skype, animated colored graphs and bar charts crept along, their real-time results bobbing up and down as the test proceeded. The display showed the number of requests per second of the various components of the BurnRate software and included the number of processes, amount of bandwidth consumed, and overall response time.

At last, the test concluded and the final report showed the totals and averages; all fell within the desired target ranges.

BurnRate was done—and it was flawless.

For a moment, no one on either team moved, as if they were afraid to jinx the results. Then Ravi gave a loud "Whoop!" and started to clap.

The floodgates broke.

A cacophony of clapping, laughter, hooting, and back-slapping erupted from both continents. Lance's team and Felipe simultaneously started trying to give each other credit for a job well done. Marco and Ravi exchanged their characteristic air high five through the big screen as Sebastián shook his head at them, grinning. Pete broadcasted a congratulations in Spanish that sparked a fresh round of applause. Almendra and Marion—who had each other up directly on their laptop screens—started talking a mile a minute.

The strain drained from Jason's shoulders as he watched the celebration. For the first time in days, the screwed-up muscles around his eyes, jaw, and mouth began to relax. He was more exhausted than he'd ever been in his life. But, more than that, he was incredibly proud of what they'd accomplished.

They hadn't just made the deadline. They had made a great product. He smiled.

Don't look now, Rick Looney. We finally broke your curse.

⁕—————⁕

The consumers agreed.

Within two weeks of BurnRate's launch, it had generated enough rave reviews to start attracting some serious attention.

Within three weeks, it had been featured in twenty-eight of the most widely accessed fitness magazines, blogs, and radio and television programs in the United States.

Four weeks after launch, sales had gone through the roof, leaving both the competition and ShapeShift's previous numbers in the dust. Thirty days in, it was clear that they weren't just going to hit the target of $50 million in revenue. They were going to shatter it. Everywhere he went—biking, the grocery store, the dentist—Jason caught glimpses of BurnRate on people's wrists. They'd expanded their color options from RunWay's green and yellow, branching out to include teal, fuchsia, black, bright purple, and orange. Paula had all but pounced on the orange one.

"Why did you pick a yellow one?" she asked Jason when she saw his choice. "Aren't you sick of yellow and green?"

"Everyone on the development team went with yellow," Jason told her.

She raised an eyebrow at him. "So that you can identify each other during capture the flag?"

"No—but not a bad silver lining." Jason smiled and explained. "Yellow is the dominant color in the Colombian flag."

As the days went on and people began to tap into the full potential of the app's interactive features, the BurnRate love raced through social media like wildfire. One of Lisbeth's marketing videos went viral, garnering more than three million views on YouTube in the space of a week—which drove another spike in sales and generated even more enthusiasm for the product.

The VCs loved that the consumers loved it.

"They've tripled our valuation," Scott announced to the leadership about a month after the launch.

"*Tripled?*" Michael repeated, his jowls slack with disbelief.

"Tripled," Scott confirmed. His eyes smiled, and for once his forehead didn't look like it was bearing the weight of the world. "We're at the top of our game and light years ahead of the competition, they said. Everyone will receive extra compensation. Well done," he added, looking at Jason.

"Guess this means we have to stop calling you Rick Looney, huh?" Lisbeth grinned at him as they left the meeting.

"All good things must come to an end," Jason told her. "All not-good things, too, lucky for me," he added under his breath. Then he said, sincerely, "Really, Lisbeth, I never could have done it without Patrick's guidance—and I probably wouldn't have signed on with him at all if you hadn't nudged me into it. Not in time to pull off BurnRate by the deadline, anyway. Thank you."

She waved him off, a teal BurnRate on her wrist. "My brother owes his career to my nudging," she laughed. "You're in good company."

When the numbers came in a couple days later, "extra compensation" turned out to be the understatement of the decade. Jason reread his new contract four times to make sure he wasn't missing something. He wasn't. They'd given him a 20 percent raise, plus a hefty bonus and additional stock options.

Well, he thought, *we won't be moving back to New Jersey for a while*—and smiled.

All was right with the world.

⸻

BurnRate wasn't the only triumphant success over adversity. After almost seven months of struggle and frustration, the backyard was finally—gloriously—complete.

The same afternoon Mike told him that the last of the equipment had been removed from the premises, Jason rang Paula at the clinic.

"They're done," he told her.

"No."

"Yes."

"All of it? The mess? It's gone?"

"Every last shovel," Jason confirmed. "Can you get off work early? I know it'll take a miracle, but I figured I'd ask."

"One miracle deserves another," Paula told him. "I'll see you at home."

Jason was in such a good mood that he DoorDashed the expensive French takeout himself, to surprise her. "We need it," he said, smiling at her look of shock when she walked through the sliding glass door onto the back deck and saw the familiar, fragrant containers laid out on their round stone table. "To celebrate our emancipation from the landscapers."

"I knew marrying you was a good idea," Paula mumbled, sliding the glass door shut behind her.

They leisurely made their way through a three-course meal and most of a bottle of wine, then abandoned the stone table in favor of their new reclining patio swing, where they lingered for the better part of three hours, listening to the waterfall and watching sunset turn to dusk, then dusk turn to nightfall. Paula's meticulously chosen koi drifted peacefully in their pond. As it grew darker, the night lighting in the yard came up, illuminating the water and the bases of the two palm trees.

Jason inhaled a deep breath and released it again, his fingers loosely twined with Paula's. The moon rose, and it was quiet—nothing broke the stillness but the sound of running water and the occasional stray chorus of crickets. The perpetual mess of scattered tools and materials was gone. It had been an uphill battle, to say the least. But they'd made it.

Everything was finally perfect.

Eventually, the wind started to pick up, heralding an incoming storm. They stayed on the swing until Paula's hair had blown into her face one too many times.

"All right, that does it," she sighed, pushing it behind her ear again. She turned her head on the swing and raised an eyebrow at Jason. "Bed?" she said.

He kissed her.

"Bed," he agreed.

An earsplitting crack too dense to be thunder jolted Jason out of bed at five o'clock in the morning.

A glance to his right showed him that Paula—hair on end and eyes wide—was on her feet, too. He heard her behind him as he sprinted downstairs, heart banging and nerves screaming with shock. *Armageddon?* he thought, his mind strangely sharp and hazy at once.

It wasn't Armageddon.

It was worse.

Jason pushed through the back sliding glass door with Paula at his heels, just in time to see the second palm tree falling slowly, like a giant, in the direction of the rock waterfall. The first had blown over in the wind and hit it, sparking a domino effect.

Everything happened in seconds.

The second palm tree smashed into the waterfall on the raised embankment.

The waterfall collapsed, breaking a water main.

The deluge from the water main caused a landslide, and half the embankment collapsed into the swimming pool.

The swimming pool overflowed, saturating the koi pond with toxic chlorine water.

And the mud from the embankment clogged up the recirculation pumps, making them strain and groan like the most enormous, horrible chorus of bullfrogs Jason had ever heard.

He dove for the emergency shut-off valve for the water as Paula dove for her fish. The valve was around the corner, by the wall in the side yard. It took Jason two tries to yank the plastic cover off. All the while, he could hear the roar of the water in the background, as if the Hoover Dam itself were collapsing. Finally, the cover came free.

He reached into the space, grabbed the handle of the valve, and yanked it to the right.

The screechy sound of the water flow being cut off grated against his eardrums. Then, the roar in the background eased . . . faded . . . stopped.

Jason heaved a breath and strode back around to the backyard.

The destruction made him dizzy. Mud, debris, rock, broken palm fronds, cracked flagstones—the wreckage would do any category-five hurricane proud. In the middle of it all stood Paula, shell shocked and mud smeared, not a single rescued koi to show for her half-dive into the pond.

Jason walked up to her, but found he couldn't speak. They stood together in the middle of the devastation, struggling to process the impossible.

Finally, after what felt like minutes, Jason found his voice. "Good thing you didn't name them," he said, jerking his chin weakly in the direction of the koi pond.

Paula made a strangled noise in her throat, her face a frozen mask of trauma. It took her a few more tries to form whole words. "Does the insurance cover this?" she managed.

"Yes," Jason nodded.

"How long to clean it up?"

"A month. Easy."

They stood in silence for another minute, taking in the ruins around them. Then, "Paris?" Paula said.

"Paris," Jason agreed. He ran a hand through his hair, shook his head, and sighed. "But we have to stop in Colombia for a wedding first."

TWENTY-ONE

The Successful Version

"That's incredible. You pulled all of that off in *six months?*"

The question came from an American named Ricardo, one of Marion's wedding guests on the groom's side, who happened to be a VP of engineering himself at a company four times the size of ShapeShift. He and Jason were standing off to one side of the enormous terrace where the reception was being held, trying to talk over the pounding beat of the music.

Marion had been right to trust Almendra and her sister with the wedding. Even Jason had to admit that all of this was a healthy step up from the Computer History Museum. The Colombian venue was a resort built into the mountains with a view of the city below. They'd held the ceremony at sunset, and Almendra had been Marion's maid of honor.

"Really?" Paula whispered in Jason's ear when the wedding party walked out. "No sisters? She didn't have any close friends?"

Jason felt a smile tug at the corner of his mouth. He shrugged. "She does now," he whispered back.

When night fell after the ceremony, they'd released the party onto the terrace—an organic half-moon with stone railing, warm flagstones, and a huge trellis-canopy of vines wrapped in an extravaganza of tiny white lights. Nicely dressed servers wandered through the crowd with trays of champagne and the Colombian version of tapas—not to mention occasional shots of *aguardiente*. Paula gave her seal of approval to the latter.

"This stuff is good for the memory," she declared after her second or third shot.

"Really?" Jason arched an eyebrow at her.

"Yeah," Paula grinned, half-yelling into his ear over the music. "The more of it I drink, the less I remember the backyard!"

Not long after that, she'd been willingly taken captive by a gaggle of partying Colombian and American women on their way to the dance floor. And they weren't the only ones having a good time. Everywhere he looked, the terrace was peppered with developers from both the ShapeShift and the MedellínTech teams, most of them wearing the yellow BurnRate wristbands Jason had brought for them beneath their nice jackets and shirtsleeves. They looked like they were at a family reunion, laughing and patting each other on the back, the Colombians teaching the Americans Spanish words and then teasing them about "communication issues" when the Americans pronounced them wrong. Somewhere among the cheerful mayhem, Jason heard a faint, "Marco!" "Polo!"

The groom had introduced him to Ricardo shortly after Paula had been spirited away.

"This is Rick de Los Angeles, not to be confused with Rick de Bogotá over there," he smiled, jerking his chin in the direction of a clapping Colombian man who seemed to be trying to organize a conga line.

"Please, call me Rick de LA!" the American Ricardo said with a laugh.

Marion's new husband laughed with him. "We need a system for organizing all the Ricardos around here," he chuckled. "Anyway, Marion thought the two of you should meet. She said you'd have a lot to talk about." He threw a fond glance over his shoulder at Marion, who was bright eyed, flushed, and laughing, a glass of champagne in one hand and the other hand braced on Almendra's shoulder for support. "I'd better get back to her," he grinned, and went.

Marion was right: Rick de Los Angeles and Jason did have plenty to talk about.

Within five minutes, Ricardo had confessed to facing the same personnel, budget, and deadline challenges at his large company that Jason had recently defeated at his start-up. He told Ricardo the whole story and confirmed that, yes, the ShapeShift and MedellínTech teams had pulled everything off in six months.

"We're planning on outsourcing some additional food databases to India next month," he told Ricardo. "The team we found down there has a top-notch data-entry operation. They're experts at accurately capturing information digitally, and they deliver it all with an index and metadata, so it's easy to integrate into software products. We're also going to outsource a new machine learning algorithm to a company I visited in Belarus to improve the accuracy of food recognition for the next release."

"Do you think outsourcing software development would work for a larger company?" Ricardo asked him, eyes piercing.

"Absolutely," Jason nodded. He knew for a fact that Patrick had helped plenty of large corporations. Setting his champagne on the low wall beside them, he reached into his wallet and started thumbing through business cards. "Here," he shouted over the din, "I'll give you the number of the guy who got me through it. His name's Patrick."

"Another Rick? Really?" Ricardo shouted back, smiling.

"No—*Pat*rick," Jason repeated, louder than before. He finally found the card he was looking for and pulled it free, but before he could hand it over, they were interrupted by the conga line.

"De LA!" hollered the other Rick, grabbing Ricardo's arm and yanking him into the line.

"De Bogotá!" Ricardo laughed, allowing himself to be led away. "I'll be back!" he called to Jason as the dance line swallowed him.

Jason had to laugh along as he watched them go, conga-ing away into the crowd like true Colombians: with passion. Really, he mused, Patrick *would* make a pretty good third musketeer. Heck, he was almost a Rick. Rick de LA, Rick de Bogotá, and Rick de Laney.

. . . wait.

He stared at the card in his hand. Patrick Delaney.

Pat-*rick* De-*laney*.

Rick Looney.

No way.

Impulsively, Jason dialed the number on the card himself.

He was thrown for yet another loop when an actual receptionist answered the phone. "One World Outsourcing Solutions," she said smoothly.

"Uh—I'd like to talk to Patrick, please," Jason managed, pressing one hand over his free ear to block out the music on the terrace.

A moment later, Patrick's voice came on the line.

"This is Patrick," he said.

"It's *you*!" Jason blurted.

"You were expecting the Dalai Lama?" Patrick replied, amused.

Jason ignored him. "It was you, the whole time!" he insisted. "*You're* Rick Looney—aren't you?"

There was a pause from the other end of the phone. Then Patrick erupted in laughter.

"You caught me red-handed, chief." Jason could practically hear him grinning as he confessed. "I didn't just leave town after my outsourcing train wreck, all those years ago. I left the country. I was determined to figure out what went wrong."

"And you did," Jason said, the pieces rapidly coming together in his mind.

"And I did," Patrick confirmed. "I visited dozens of outsourcing companies around the world until I finally understood how the beast worked. Of course, then it wasn't a beast anymore," he chuckled. "I've been helping poor unfortunate souls like yourself outsource software development ever since."

"You never told me," Jason accused, but he was smiling.

"What can I say?" Patrick sighed. "I had a sneaking suspicion that broadcasting myself as 'Rick Looney's Software Outsourcing Solutions' would be less than ideal for business."

"Right. Speaking of which, things are looking up, aren't they? I see you finally got yourself a receptionist," Jason pointed out.

"Yeah," Patrick said, and again Jason could hear the grin in his voice. "To keep the throngs of clients in line."

They talked for another minute about Patrick's growing success before the blaring music became too much for Jason to handle. "I'd better get going," he said.

"Live it up, chief. That's what you've got a life for," Patrick told him. Then he added, "And do me a favor—keep my secret identity amongst friends, will you?"

"Yeah, of course," Jason agreed. He saw Ravi approaching him and waved. "I'll see you about the Indian and Belarusian outsourcing teams when I get back."

"I'll see if I can fit you into my calendar," Patrick joked.

Ravi, swigging a glass of champagne, arrived just as Jason hung up the phone.

Who else counted as "amongst friends," if not Ravi?

"Ravi," Jason told him, "get this. Patrick Delaney is actually Rick Looney. The real one."

Ravi laughed so hard that champagne almost came out of his nose. He got the choking under control—and then kept laughing.

"So you really did become Rick Looney after all!" he managed when he finally regained his power of speech, wiping tears of laughter from his eyes. "Just the successful version."

Jason picked up laughing where Ravi left off. Then he lifted his own glass of champagne off the wall and clinked it against Ravi's.

"To the successful version," he grinned. "May he go down in history all over again."

BIBLIOGRAPHY

- *The Phoenix Project* by Gene Kim and Kevin Behr
- *Predictability* by Steve Bockman
- *The Deadline: A Novel about Project Management* by Tom DeMarco
- *When Cultures Collide* by Richard D. Lewis
- *The Art of Scalability* by Martin L. Abbott and Michael T. Fisher
- *Microservices Patterns and Applications* by Lucas Krause
- *Building Microservices* by Sam Newman
- *The Culture Map* by Erin Meyer
- *Probably Approximately Correct* by Leslie Valiant
- *The Master Algorithm* by Pedro Domingos
- *Software Architecture in Practice* by Len Bass and Paul Clements
- *Managing the Unmanageable: Rules, Tools, and Insights for Managing Software People and Teams* by Mickey W. Mantle and Ron Lichty

Appendix A: The Seven Keys of Software Outsourcing

Colombia, Here We Come?

If you finish this book thinking, "This is easy; I'll just outsource my software development to Colombia!" then we hate to tell you, but you're missing the point. This book isn't about outsourcing to Colombia, specifically. We easily could have written about Jason selecting his partner company anywhere else, from Argentina to Vietnam, or Bangladesh, Belarus, or Bolivia. In our travels, we have found smart people and great software outsourcing companies in most countries around the world. That's a central tenet of this book.

But with so many choices available, an organized process is needed so you can wisely select your partner, do so in a reasonable amount of time, and reduce the risk of choosing the wrong partner. Jason's story would have had a dramatically different ending if he had just selected that company the venture capital investor recommended. Instead, he relied on Patrick's help to guide him through a studied and careful selection process that led to a successful and happy outcome.

That's the purpose of this appendix—to give you solid guidelines and principles to guide your selection of your own global software outsourcing partner.

First, let's consider this question.

Why Outsource Your Software Development?

Contrary to popular belief, outsourcing is not about finding cheap programmers! The truth is that there is a shortage of software engineering talent in Western countries that adds huge delays in building your own software development team. The result of this shortage is often a lag in getting your software product to market or a problem keeping your employees productive once your software app has been deployed.

And if you do build your own software engineering team, are you also able to provide the right work environment, business culture, and best practices to create great and innovative software? Most companies are simply not qualified to develop software well. Software outsourcing gives you the ability to hire the expertise you need.

And yes, it also saves money. These days, employing your own onsite development team is an expensive luxury. The average hourly rate for employees in the United States is about $85, including benefits, overhead, etc. Individual consultants and consulting firms in the United States charge at a much higher hourly rate, often more than $120 per hour.

In comparison, competitive global outsourcing developers charge between $20 and $45 per hour for experienced programmers, and sometimes less, depending on the skill level of the programmers, their country's location, and the size and length of your engagement.

Outsourcing gives you the opportunity to cut your software development costs by 60 percent, and more in some cases. And more importantly than just lowering costs, global outsourcing provides these other major benefits:

- Fast ramp-up of your programming team
- Flexibility in growing and shrinking your team as needed
- Higher speed and better quality, because you have access to a very large pool of talent
- Technical expertise that is difficult for you to hire locally
- Improved innovation, by leveraging your development team's experience working with multiple clients

- Best practices of software development and participation in the latest technology trends
- Expanded work day when offshore developers are several time zones away

Many companies prefer to have an internal development team to enable easy communication between team members. Today, the Internet enables similar communications capabilities between your company and an outsourced team, giving you ease in exchanging ideas as well as tremendous cost savings.

Many individuals who are new to software outsourcing harbor common fears about it, including lack of control, unclear standards and certifications, loss of intellectual property, and lack of cultural alignment. However, these fears are rooted in the traditional idea of outsourcing: I give you a task, describe what I need done, and expect you to do it as quickly and cheaply as possible—period. That's not outsourcing; that's out-tasking!

Real outsourcing, by contrast, is hiring a company to provide a service better, faster, and more expertly than you can do on your own, even if you can hire enough employees to do it.

Modern software outsourcing is a collaborative endeavor between you and your outsourced team. Instead of a group of yes-men, you hire smart, extroverted problem solvers who will take equal responsibility for the delivery of your product, and who will challenge each other to solve development problems.

It takes real work to find companies that have a true love and passion for the art of software development, but they do exist. Accelerance's Seven Keys of Software Outsourcing are designed to help you find them and then work with them to achieve the highest-quality results.

Key 1: Great Developers Are Everywhere

Brilliant, educated developers exist all over the world. Accelerance has spent ten years traveling the globe to identify, screen, and partner with the best software development firms available. This is what we've seen:

Many people unfamiliar with software outsourcing assume that the quality of onshore developers is higher by default. The truth is that good offshore companies hire extremely educated, experienced, and talented people. Many are developers who have attended top global and US universities. They aren't just maintenance programmers. They're highly trained individuals with very advanced knowledge in the latest technologies, and they actually want a challenge.

You just need to know how to find them.

Key 2: Focus on Your Vision

One of the most fundamental obstacles to finding a good outsourcing team is getting out of your own way. The key to this is focusing on your vision.

You can't do everything yourself. Software development is a complex process, and if you want good results fast, you need a team of talented people on your side—not just one "rock star" developer. You can't afford to spend 90 percent of your time figuring out how to build the product and only 10 percent of your time on delivering it.

As a leader, your focus should be on making sure that your product gets to market, and that it's successful when it gets there. The best way to accomplish this is to spend your time working at a higher, strategic level. You can add the most value by thinking through and constantly adjusting your product's market fit, longer-term product road map, product sequencing, and pricing iterations.

When you focus on your vision for the success of your company and allow everything else—including software development—to become supplementary, you empower your organization to attain maximum success.

Key 3: In-Person Investigation Is Critical

The first step to finding a strong outsourcing company is preliminary research, during which you do the following:

- Make sure the company meets all of your technical requirements.
- Check that the company has recently done the kind of work you need (or close to it).
- Get references from the company's other clients—past, present, and recent.
- Obtain a proposal from the company that includes the ramp-up time and cost for your development team.

However, pre-vetting alone is not enough to guarantee you an outstanding outsourcing partner. After you've narrowed down a list of strong candidates, Accelerance strongly recommends visiting your potential companies in person, even if they have been evaluated and certified by us. This is because you're not buying widgets; you are partnering with people. You need a team that you can build a good relationship with, and it's difficult to get a true feel for that human connection by video call. An in-person investigation is the best way to learn whether you'll be able to build a strong working relationship with your outsourcers.

Practical reasons for visiting your potential outsourcers in person should also be taken into account. During your in-person investigation, confirm that your potential company

- has actually done the kind of work you need, as it claimed during your preliminary research.
- is guided by qualified, intelligent leaders who are setting

high standards for hiring quality developers.
- has developed effective hiring, training, and retention processes.
- is willing to show you the things you want to see.
- has technical leads and senior people who can answer your questions about technologies, testing processes and methodologies, communication challenges, and new trends.
- uses a top-notch software development process.
- makes you feel welcome.

Your potential company should also give you a tour of the facility. On the tour, verify that

- the building is nice by the standards of the country you're visiting.
- security measures for the protection of intellectual property are in place (e.g., soundproof rooms and doors with security access codes).
- the developers themselves seem happy and collaboration and good rapport are taking place.

Key 4: Quality Matters as Much as Price

When making your final decision about your outsourcing company, it's key to consider that quality matters as much as price.

"Quality" is not defined by technical skill and experience alone. It also includes a team's ability to learn, work collaboratively, maintain clear communication, and fit in with your company's culture and core values. In other words, you need EQ (emotional intelligence quotient) as much as or even more than you need IQ. Innovation, great leadership, and high hiring standards likewise need to be factored into your overall assessment of an outsourcing company's quality.

You want to strike a healthy balance between quality and price when evaluating your outsourcing candidates. The offshore hourly rate for the same level of quality you'd expect to find in an onshore developer generally ranges between 25 and 65 percent lower than you'd pay at home. For example, if the onsite developer you need happened to cost $120 an hour all in, you could expect to pay an offshore developer with a comparable skill set something between $35 and $75 an hour.

Be extremely wary of hiring outsourcers based on a low price alone. You can find developers who charge less than $20 per hour, but you'll more than likely be engaging solopreneur freelancers and companies that cut major corners, which can potentially include terrible infrastructure, horrendous working conditions, and contracted freelancers instead of developer employees. At that point, the low price tag is just not worth the risk.

Ultimately, you should feel like you're getting everything you're looking for from your outsourcing company at a fair price. If a team costs more, it may be because it has better equipment, more overhead, higher EQ, greater flexibility, and so on. Even if you're paying more for one global outsourcer than another, remember that at the end of the day, you're still paying far less than what you'd pay locally.

Outsourcing gives you the opportunity to get things done faster and cheaper, but remember that faster and cheaper is less important than the quality of the product. Keep in mind that you're not looking for a Ferrari or a Yugo. You want a Toyota: a company that is solid, stable, low maintenance, and cost effective, with years of experience and tens of thousands of hours of engineering on its résumé to back it up. This is the balance you want to strike between talent and cost.

Key 5: Think Like a Partner and Embrace Cultural Differences

After you hire the outsourcing company that is the best fit for you, you will very probably experience an acclimation period as you and your team get used to working with your new partners.

Minor cultural differences may arise that may seem irritating at first, and you will need to remember not to throw the baby out with the bathwater.

First and foremost, treat your outsourcing company like a partner. Communicate clearly; give them time to learn your product, company history, and culture; and take the time to get their perspective on what you are pursuing. Taking the time to build a relationship with your key contacts in the outsourcing company will pay off in spades, particularly when you have to navigate challenges or project complexity.

Cultural differences abound. For example, in Asia, it is impolite to say "no." Therefore, individuals from these countries communicate less directly than Americans do, and you need to become aware of the phrases that actually mean "no" when you begin working with them—such as "That will be difficult" in India. At the other end of the spectrum, Eastern European cultures are so straightforward that they can come across as rude or offensive. When working with individuals from this region, it's important not to take blunt comments personally, because the comments aren't personal; they're cultural.

Some countries are big on saving face. Again, in cases like these, the learning curve is to let them save face instead of turning everything into a personal battle, always remembering that the focus should stay on getting what you need and maintaining a good relationship with your outsourcing partner. (Remember too that Americans have their own ways of saving face; we do it so often and so naturally that we tend not to be aware of it.) You could also run into miscommunication glitches over things like English idioms. For instance, you might say something like, "Where do you stand on this?" and your outsourcer might respond, "I'm standing right here in my office."

During the acclimation period, the important thing is to keep your eye on the bottom line. If you're getting a good-quality product and are basically aligned with your outsourcing team at a core level, then you're where you need to be.

Don't look at cultural differences as a barrier. Instead, go into the relationship accepting, embracing, and even enjoying the differences you encounter. Focus on the things you and your outsourcers have in common and can get excited about together. If you can do this, then you can create a strong overall process for your software development.

Key 6: The Relationship Is as Important as Technical Requirements and Capabilities

The art of software development requires true partnership, collaboration, and equal investment from both your onsite and outsourcing teams. You should never go into an outsourcing agreement with a "command and control" mentality, because the more you do, the more you compromise the quality of your product.

On the other hand, building a strong relationship with your outsourcing team will get you the best possible results. When you develop a sense of trust and reciprocity with your outsourcers, you create a bond that makes them want to do their best for you. People—regardless of nationality—feel a much stronger sense of obligation to deliver to someone who knows and cares about them.

The core of a good relationship with your outsourcing partner involves effective communication, understanding the outsourcing team's values and culture, and a genuine personal connection with the people you're working with. Your outsourcing team shouldn't be separate from your onsite team; it should be an extension of it. You should be friends, and you should have each other's backs.

To keep the relationship going strong, Accelerance recommends visiting your outsourcing team members in their country at least once per quarter to maintain an open channel of communication. You can invite your outsourcing team to come visit you as well.

Although this practice may seem expensive on the surface, the investment will pay off significantly in your business in the long run.

Key 7: Everything You Invest in Hiring a Good Outsourcing Team Will Return to You Threefold

If you are casual about selecting a good outsourcing partner in the first place, the odds are high that you'll pay for it later. However, if you put the effort into choosing a top-of-the-line company from the beginning, the reverse is true: your decision will pay you back in ways that you never could have foreseen.

The idea of "investing" in your outsourcing team includes money, but it goes far beyond money alone. It also includes preliminary research, time, and especially relationship building. An innovative, passionate, and competent team will be able to support not just your original goals, but also objectives that go far beyond what you initially imagined you would use them for.

As your company expands, a good outsourcing team will more than likely be able to seamlessly expand with you. This can prove to be one of the most rewarding parts of outsourcing software development, when all is said and done.

Accelerance: *Software without Borders*

You can learn more about Accelerance's in-depth, step-by-step process for hiring a great outsourcing team in Steve's first book, *Software without Borders*. We also offer one-on-one consultations to match you with the right software development company by understanding your personal business model, technology requirements, and preferences. To learn more, visit www.accelerance.com.

Appendix B: The "Foo" Coding Puzzle

Problem

Jason asks, "You're given a function, 'foo,' that represents a biased coin. When foo is called, it returns a 0 with 25 percent probability, and a 1 with 75 percent probability. In any programming language, write a new function that uses foo but returns 0 and 1 each with 50 percent probability."

Solution

The solution is to somehow get two cases with equal probability. Each time we call foo(), it will return a 0 with 25 percent probability and a 1 with 75 percent probability. The trick is to find some sequence of foo() calls that has a 50/50 probability. After just two calls, we have the solution. Here are the probabilities of the four possible results of the two consecutive calls of foo():

(0, 0): The probability to get 0 followed by
     another 0 = 0.25 * 0.25 = 0.0625

(0, 1): The probability to get 0 followed by
     a 1 = 0.75 * 0.25 = 0.1875

(1, 0): The probability to get 1 followed by
     a 0 = 0.25 * 0.75 = 0.1875

(1, 1): The probability to get 1 followed by another
     another 1 = 0.75 * 0.75 = 0.5625

So the two pairs (0, 1) and (1, 0) will be generated with equal probability from two calls of foo().

The new function—bar()—should return a 0 or a 1 for only the middle two cases, returning a 1 for (0, 1) and returning a 0 for (1, 0). For the other (0, 0) and (1, 1) cases, bar() recurses until it gets either of the above two cases.

Here's the code in JavaScript:

```
Def bar():
   if (foo() == 0){
     var x = foo() // Call foo() again after getting a 0
        if( x == 1) {//
            return x  // Got a (0, 1) return a 1
        } else {
           bar()
        }
   } else {
          var y = foo() // Call foo() a again after a 1
          if( y == 0) {
              return y // Got a (1, 0) return a 0
          } else {
              bar()
          }
      }
   }
```

Credit for the puzzle goes to http://stackoverflow.com/questions/5051970/an-interview-question-about-probability, and for the best online answer to http://www.geeksforgeeks.org/print-0-and-1-with-50-probability/.

INDEX

163

MySQL 10, 72

nearshoring 27
Nepal 61, 64
networking event, Engineering
    Leadership Forum 8, 16, 20,
    21–28, 40, 41
New Jersey 15, 19, 28, 111, 119,
    127, 133, 140
Node.JS 34
NoSQL 10, 31, 35, 49, 72, 117,
    129, 130, 131
Nutrition. *See under* software, new
    features of

Objective-C 10
Offshoring. *See* outsourcing
O'Malley's 3
One World Software Outsourcing
    Solutions
    as a company 22, 25, 39, 56,
        124, 128, 147
    database 50, 54, 58, 80
    Partner Selection App 56–58
onshoring 154, 156
Oracle 10, 72
outsourcing
    benefits of 23, 24, 125, 126
    failed approaches to 12, 33,
        42–46, 133–135, 148
    fears regarding 9, 11, 12, 14–15,
        24, 36, 41–42, 93, 115, 153
    objections to 7, 11
    promise of 15, 26–27, 146
    reasons for 7, 23–24, 146,
        151–153
    Seven Keys of. *See* Seven Keys
        of Software Outsourcing
    software 21–27, 41, 42, 46, 92,
        116, 151–154

successes with 30–31, 36, 119,
    139–140
outsourcing companies
    communication challenges with
        86, 92–95, 101, 103–104,
        158–159
    database. *See under* One
        World Software Outsourcing
        Solutions
    decision-making process for
        46–49, 56–60, 80–82, 84–87
    in-person investigation of 46,
        59, 64, 68–72, 78–82, 87,
        146, 148, 155–156
    investing in 25, 47, 83–86,
        104–107, 126, 159–160
    levels of experience of 24, 34,
        35, 47, 49, 78, 85, 130, 134,
        152, 154, 155, 157
    onboarding. *See under* teams
    pre-judgment of 18, 50, 61, 73
    processes of 70–72, 78–79, 85,
        92–93, 95, 112, 137, 156
    proposals from 33, 34–35
    top 100 33

Pakistan 26
palm trees 18, 120–123, 133, 141,
    142, 143
Palo Alto 8
Papa John's 34
Paris 54, 143
Partner Selection App 56–58
partnerships 25, 46, 49, 56, 82,
    88, 103, 105, 126, 151, 154,
    155, 157–160
Peace Corps 10, 11, 96
pen, as symbol 4, 5, 6, 9, 12, 13,
    14, 16, 21, 22, 30, 33, 41, 42,
    47, 58, 59, 60, 61, 83, 88, 96,

ABOUT THE AUTHORS

 **STEVE MEZAK** is the founder and CEO of Accelerance, Inc., a leader in global software development outsourcing. With more than thirty years in the IT industry, Steve is a technical entrepreneur and internationally recognized outsourcing expert and speaker. He oversees Accelerance's operations, drives strategy for business development, and leads recruitment of international partners.

Steve founded Accelerance in 2001 with the goal of helping clients find outsourced partner firms that best serve their technical needs and align with their corporate culture. Throughout his career, Steve has guided hundreds of IT executives through the strategic advantages of outsourcing their software development. Steve has spent more than fifteen years traveling the globe and interviewing thousands of software development teams to build Accelerance's network of partner firms. He is also the author of *Software without Borders: A Step-by-Step Guide to Outsourcing Your Software Development.*

 **ANDY HILLIARD** is the president of Accelerance, Inc., a leader in global software development outsourcing. An IT industry veteran with more than twenty years of experience, Andy has a proven track record of taking a personalized approach to matching businesses with software development partners that are best suited to fulfilling their individual needs.

Andy leads Accelerance's overall operations and cultivates strategic partnerships to expand its network of software development firms worldwide. He helps companies optimize their software development efforts by leveraging his diverse experience, including time spent as a Peace Corps volunteer in Latin America, a division manager at India-centric Cognizant, and a founder of his own software company in Costa Rica.

CPSIA information can be obtained
at www.ICGtesting.com
Printed in the USA
FSOW02n1011130117
29442FS

9 780977 826827